TENNESSEE STATE PARKS BUCKET JOURNAL

Visit 110 State Parks, Historic Sites,
Natural Areas, & Tennessee Treasures

This book belongs to

_____

If found please call

_____

"**I only went out** for a walk, and finally concluded to stay out till sundown, for going out, I found, was really going in." ~John Muir

"**Although I do love oceans**, deserts, and other wild landscapes, it is only mountains that beckon me with the sort of painful magnetic pull to walk deeper and deeper into their beauty. They keep me continuously wanting to know more, feel more, see more To become more." ~Victoria Erickson

"**The Smoky Mountains** are a rare jewel...Why not have a place where you can still see the stars? There is value to keeping things primitive." ~James Dawson

TENNESSEE STATE PARKS BUCKET JOURNAL

The State of Tennessee is a patchwork landscape of mountains, waterfalls, fertile valleys, and long tree-covered ridges. You could spend years exploring more than 500 waterfalls, 656 hiking trails, and over 10,000 caves!

This breathtaking scenery encourages everyone who visits (or lives there) to get out and explore.

Some of the parks in the journal are well known and some are less traveled, all are waiting for you to discover their unique qualities.

In this Tennessee State Parks Bucket Journal, **you will find individual pages for 110 state parks, historic sites, natural areas, and Tennessee treasures** in the beautiful state. Many allow for overnight camping and all are great for day use trips.

This bucket journal is different. It gives you the ability to create your own unique exploration of whichever state park or historic site you choose

How to Use Your Tennessee State Parks Bucket Journal

Parks that offer camping or other accommodations are on Yellow pages.
- Search out details about the state park or recreational site by using the website URL provided.
- Have fun planning the things you want to see on the left side of the 2-page spread.
- This is best done before you take your trip, but can be done while you are out exploring.
- On the right side, chronicle everything that you do and experience. Included is space for journaling and reflection about your stay in the park.

Parks that are Day Use Area Only are on orange pages.
- Day use parks are still fun to visit, even if you can't sleep there.
- Visit them when you are staying at other overnight parks or use them as day trip excursions to get out and explore.

The Tennessee State Parks Bucket Journal will become a living memory for your trips and adventures as you discover the wonders around you.

Enjoy exploring the beauty that is Tennessee!

TABLE OF CONTENTS

SHA: *State Historic Area* SHP: *State Historic Park* SP: *State Park*

TABLE OF CONTENTS

SHA: *State Historic Area* SHP: *State Historic Park* SP: *State Park*

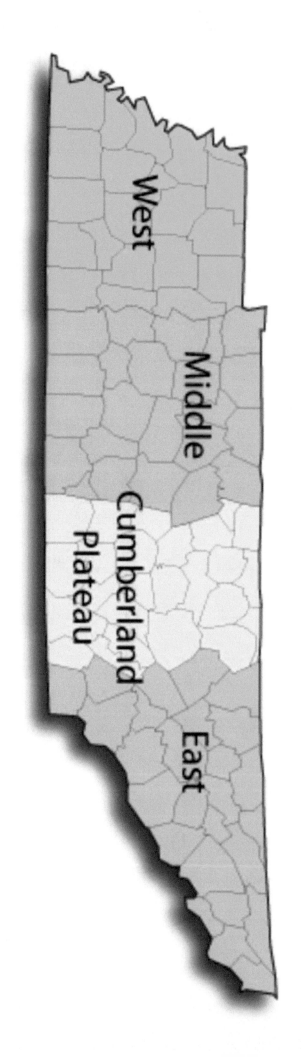

West

Middle

Cumberland
Plateau

East

West Region

Nathan Bedford Forrest State Park

City: Eva   County: Benton

Plan your trip: https://tnstateparks.com/parks/nathan-bedford-forrest

Activities:

- ☐ Birding
- ☐ Biking
- ☐ Boating
- ☐ Caving
- ☐ Disc Golf / Golf
- ☐ Fishing
- ☐ Hiking
- ☐ Horseback Riding
- ☐ Hunting
- ☐ Interpretive Programs

- ☐ Mountain Biking
- ☐ Paddling
- ☐ Rock Climbing
- ☐ Swimming
- ☐ Waterfalls
- ☐ Water sports
- ☐ Wildlife Viewing
- ☐
- ☐
- ☐
- ☐

- ☐
- ☐
- ☐
- ☐
- ☐
- ☐
- ☐
- ☐
- ☐
- ☐
- ☐

Facilities:

- ☐ ADA
- ☐ Picnic sites
- ☐ Restrooms
- ☐ Showers
- ☐ Trailer Access
- ☐ Visitor center
- ☐ Group Camping
- ☐ RV Camp
- ☐ Rustic Camping
- ☐ Cabins / Yurts
- ☐ Day Use Area

Notes:

Get the Facts

- ☐ Phone   731-593-6445
- ☐ Park Hours

  _____

- ☐ Reservations? ____ Y ____ N

  date made_____

- ☐ Open all year ____ Y ____ N

  dates_____

- ☐ Check in time _____
- ☐ Check out time _____
- ☐ Pet friendly _____ Y _____ N
- ☐ Max RV length _____
- ☐ Distance from home

  miles: _____

  hours: _____

- ☐ Address_____

  _____

  _____

Fees:

- ☐ Day Use $ _____
- ☐ Camp Sites $ _____
- ☐ RV Sites $ _____
- ☐ Refund policy

  _____

  _____

  _____

Make It Personal

Trip dates:

The weather was: Sunny Cloudy Rainy Stormy Snowy Foggy Warm Cold

Why I went:

How I got there: (circle all that apply)   Plane   Train   Car   Bus   Bike   Hike   RV   MC

I went with:

We stayed in (space, cabin # etc):

Most relaxing day:

Something funny:

Someone we met:

Best story told:

The kids liked this:

The best food:

Games played:

Something disappointing:

Next time I'll do this differently:

Chickasaw State Park
City: Henderson   County: Chester

Plan your trip: https://tnstateparks.com/parks/chickasaw

Activities:

- ☐ Birding
- ☐ Biking
- ☐ Boating
- ☐ Caving
- ☐ Disc Golf / Golf
- ☐ Fishing
- ☐ Hiking
- ☐ Horseback Riding
- ☐ Hunting
- ☐ Interpretive Programs

- ☐ Mountain Biking
- ☐ Paddling
- ☐ Rock Climbing
- ☐ Swimming
- ☐ Waterfalls
- ☐ Water sports
- ☐ Wildlife Viewing
- ☐
- ☐
- ☐
- ☐

- ☐
- ☐
- ☐
- ☐
- ☐
- ☐
- ☐
- ☐
- ☐
- ☐
- ☐

Facilities:

- ☐ ADA
- ☐ Picnic sites
- ☐ Restrooms
- ☐ Showers
- ☐ Trailer Access
- ☐ Visitor center
- ☐ Group Camping
- ☐ RV Camp
- ☐ Rustic Camping
- ☐ Cabins / Yurts
- ☐ Day Use Area

Notes:

Get the Facts

- ☐ Phone   731-989-5141
- ☐ Park Hours

  _____

- ☐ Reservations? ____Y ____N

  date made_____

- ☐ Open all year ____Y____N

  dates_____

- ☐ Check in time _____

- ☐ Check out time _____

- ☐ Pet friendly _____Y _____N

- ☐ Max RV length _____

- ☐ Distance from home

  miles: _____

  hours: _____

- ☐ Address_____

  _____

  _____

Fees:

- ☐ Day Use $ _____
- ☐ Camp Sites $ _____
- ☐ RV Sites $ _____
- ☐ Refund policy

  _____

  _____

  _____

Make It Personal

Trip dates: _____

The weather was: Sunny   Cloudy   Rainy   Stormy   Snowy   Foggy   Warm   Cold

Why I went: _____

_____

How I got there: (circle all that apply)   Plane   Train   Car   Bus   Bike   Hike   RV   MC

I went with: _____

We stayed in (space, cabin # etc): _____

Most relaxing day: _____

_____

Something funny: _____

_____

Someone we met: _____

_____

Best story told: _____

_____

The kids liked this: _____

_____

The best food: _____

_____

Games played: _____

_____

Something disappointing: _____

_____

Next time I'll do this differently: _____

_____

Big Hill Pond State Park
City: Pocahontas   County: Hardeman

Plan your trip: https://tnstateparks.com/parks/big-hill-pond

Activities:

- ☐ Birding
- ☐ Biking
- ☐ Boating
- ☐ Caving
- ☐ Disc Golf / Golf
- ☐ Fishing
- ☐ Hiking
- ☐ Horseback Riding
- ☐ Hunting
- ☐ Interpretive Programs
- ☐ Mountain Biking
- ☐ Paddling
- ☐ Rock Climbing
- ☐ Swimming
- ☐ Waterfalls
- ☐ Water sports
- ☐ Wildlife Viewing
- ☐
- ☐
- ☐
- ☐
- ☐
- ☐
- ☐
- ☐
- ☐
- ☐
- ☐
- ☐
- ☐
- ☐

Facilities:

- ☐ ADA
- ☐ Picnic sites
- ☐ Restrooms
- ☐ Showers
- ☐ Trailer Access
- ☐ Visitor center
- ☐ Group Camping
- ☐ RV Camp
- ☐ Rustic Camping
- ☐ Cabins / Yurts
- ☐ Day Use Area

Notes:

Get the Facts

- ☐ Phone   731-645-7967
- ☐ Park Hours

  _____

- ☐ Reservations? ____Y ____N

  date made_____

- ☐ Open all year ____Y_____N

  dates_____

- ☐ Check in time _____
- ☐ Check out time _____
- ☐ Pet friendly _____Y _____N
- ☐ Max RV length _____
- ☐ Distance from home

  miles: _____

  hours: _____

- ☐ Address_____

  _____

  _____

Fees:

- ☐ Day Use $ _____
- ☐ Camp Sites $ _____
- ☐ RV Sites $ _____
- ☐ Refund policy

  _____

  _____

  _____

Make It Personal

Trip dates: _____ | The weather was: Sunny Cloudy Rainy Stormy Snowy Foggy Warm Cold

Why I went:

_____

How I got there: (circle all that apply)   Plane   Train   Car   Bus   Bike   Hike   RV   MC

I went with:

We stayed in (space, cabin # etc):

Most relaxing day:

_____

Something funny:

_____

Someone we met:

_____

Best story told:

_____

The kids liked this:

_____

The best food:

_____

Games played:

_____

Something disappointing:

_____

Next time I'll do this differently:

_____

Pickwick Landing State Park
City: Pickwick Dam   County: Hardin

Plan your trip: https://tnstateparks.com/parks/pickwick-landing

Activities:

- ☐ Birding
- ☐ Biking
- ☐ Boating
- ☐ Caving
- ☐ Disc Golf / Golf
- ☐ Fishing
- ☐ Hiking
- ☐ Horseback Riding
- ☐ Hunting
- ☐ Interpretive Programs

- ☐ Mountain Biking
- ☐ Paddling
- ☐ Rock Climbing
- ☐ Swimming
- ☐ Waterfalls
- ☐ Water sports
- ☐ Wildlife Viewing
- ☐
- ☐
- ☐
- ☐
- ☐

- ☐
- ☐
- ☐
- ☐
- ☐
- ☐
- ☐
- ☐
- ☐
- ☐
- ☐

Facilities:

- ☐ ADA
- ☐ Picnic sites
- ☐ Restrooms
- ☐ Showers
- ☐ Trailer Access
- ☐ Visitor center
- ☐ Group Camping
- ☐ RV Camp
- ☐ Rustic Camping
- ☐ Cabins / Yurts
- ☐ Day Use Area

Notes:

Get the Facts

- ☐ Phone   731-689-3149
- ☐ Park Hours

  _____

- ☐ Reservations? ____Y ____N

  date made_____

- ☐ Open all year ____Y____N

  dates_____

- ☐ Check in time _____
- ☐ Check out time _____
- ☐ Pet friendly _____Y _____N
- ☐ Max RV length _____
- ☐ Distance from home

  miles: _____

  hours: _____

- ☐ Address_____

  _____

  _____

Fees:

- ☐ Day Use $ _____
- ☐ Camp Sites $ _____
- ☐ RV Sites $ _____
- ☐ Refund policy

  _____
  _____
  _____

Make It Personal

Trip dates: _____

The weather was: Sunny Cloudy Rainy Stormy Snowy Foggy Warm Cold

Why I went: _____

_____

How I got there: (circle all that apply) Plane Train Car Bus Bike Hike RV MC

I went with: _____

We stayed in (space, cabin # etc): _____

Most relaxing day: _____

_____

Something funny: _____

_____

Someone we met: _____

_____

Best story told: _____

_____

The kids liked this: _____

_____

The best food: _____

_____

Games played: _____

_____

Something disappointing: _____

_____

Next time I'll do this differently: _____

_____

_____

Natchez Trace State Park
City: Wildersville   County: Henderson

Plan your trip: https://tnstateparks.com/parks/natchez-trace

Activities:

- ❑ Birding
- ❑ Biking
- ❑ Boating
- ❑ Caving
- ❑ Disc Golf / Golf
- ❑ Fishing
- ❑ Hiking
- ❑ Horseback Riding
- ❑ Hunting
- ❑ Interpretive Programs

- ❑ Mountain Biking
- ❑ Paddling
- ❑ Rock Climbing
- ❑ Swimming
- ❑ Waterfalls
- ❑ Water sports
- ❑ Wildlife Viewing
- ❑
- ❑
- ❑
- ❑

- ❑
- ❑
- ❑
- ❑
- ❑
- ❑
- ❑
- ❑
- ❑
- ❑
- ❑

Facilities:

- ❑ ADA
- ❑ Picnic sites
- ❑ Restrooms
- ❑ Showers
- ❑ Trailer Access
- ❑ Visitor center
- ❑ Group Camping
- ❑ RV Camp
- ❑ Rustic Camping
- ❑ Cabins / Yurts
- ❑ Day Use Area

Notes:

Get the Facts

- ❑ Phone   731-968-3742
- ❑ Park Hours

  _____

- ❑ Reservations? ____Y ____N

  date made_____

- ❑ Open all year ____Y_____N

  dates_____

- ❑ Check in time _____
- ❑ Check out time _____
- ❑ Pet friendly _____Y _____N
- ❑ Max RV length _____
- ❑ Distance from home

  miles: _____

  hours: _____

- ❑ Address_____

  _____

  _____

Fees:

- ❑ Day Use $ _____
- ❑ Camp Sites $ _____
- ❑ RV Sites $ _____
- ❑ Refund policy

  _____

  _____

  _____

Make It Personal

Trip dates: _____ | The weather was: Sunny Cloudy Rainy Stormy Snowy Foggy Warm Cold

Why I went:
_____
_____

How I got there: (circle all that apply)   Plane   Train   Car   Bus   Bike   Hike   RV   MC
_____

I went with:
_____

We stayed in (space, cabin # etc):
_____

Most relaxing day:
_____
_____

Something funny:
_____
_____

Someone we met:
_____
_____

Best story told:
_____
_____

The kids liked this:
_____
_____

The best food:
_____
_____

Games played:
_____
_____

Something disappointing:
_____
_____

Next time I'll do this differently:
_____
_____

Paris Landing State Park
City: Buchanan   County: Henry

Plan your trip: https://tnstateparks.com/parks/paris-landing

Activities:

- ❏ Birding
- ❏ Biking
- ❏ Boating
- ❏ Caving
- ❏ Disc Golf / Golf
- ❏ Fishing
- ❏ Hiking
- ❏ Horseback Riding
- ❏ Hunting
- ❏ Interpretive Programs

- ❏ Mountain Biking
- ❏ Paddling
- ❏ Rock Climbing
- ❏ Swimming
- ❏ Waterfalls
- ❏ Water sports
- ❏ Wildlife Viewing
- ❏
- ❏
- ❏
- ❏

- ❏
- ❏
- ❏
- ❏
- ❏
- ❏
- ❏
- ❏
- ❏
- ❏
- ❏

Facilities:

- ❏ ADA
- ❏ Picnic sites
- ❏ Restrooms
- ❏ Showers
- ❏ Trailer Access
- ❏ Visitor center
- ❏ Group Camping
- ❏ RV Camp
- ❏ Rustic Camping
- ❏ Cabins / Yurts
- ❏ Day Use Area

Notes:

Get the Facts

- ❏ Phone   731-641-4465
- ❏ Park Hours

  _____

- ❏ Reservations? ____Y ____N

  date made_____
- ❏ Open all year ____Y____N

  dates_____
- ❏ Check in time _____
- ❏ Check out time _____
- ❏ Pet friendly _____Y _____N
- ❏ Max RV length _____
- ❏ Distance from home

  miles: _____

  hours: _____
- ❏ Address_____

  _____

  _____

Fees:

- ❏ Day Use $ _____
- ❏ Camp Sites $ _____
- ❏ RV Sites $ _____
- ❏ Refund policy

  _____

  _____

  _____

Make It Personal

Trip dates: _____ | The weather was: Sunny Cloudy Rainy Stormy Snowy Foggy Warm Cold

Why I went:
_____

How I got there: (circle all that apply)   Plane   Train   Car   Bus   Bike   Hike   RV   MC

I went with:
_____

We stayed in (space, cabin # etc):
_____

Most relaxing day:
_____

Something funny:
_____

Someone we met:
_____

Best story told:
_____

The kids liked this:
_____

The best food:
_____

Games played:
_____

Something disappointing:
_____

Next time I'll do this differently:
_____
_____

Reelfoot Lake State Park
City: Tiptonville   County: Lake

Plan your trip: https://tnstateparks.com/parks/reelfoot-lake

Activities:

- ❏ Birding
- ❏ Biking
- ❏ Boating
- ❏ Caving
- ❏ Disc Golf / Golf
- ❏ Fishing
- ❏ Hiking
- ❏ Horseback Riding
- ❏ Hunting
- ❏ Interpretive Programs

- ❏ Mountain Biking
- ❏ Paddling
- ❏ Rock Climbing
- ❏ Swimming
- ❏ Waterfalls
- ❏ Water sports
- ❏ Wildlife Viewing
- ❏
- ❏
- ❏

- ❏
- ❏
- ❏
- ❏
- ❏
- ❏
- ❏
- ❏
- ❏
- ❏

Facilities:

- ❏ ADA
- ❏ Picnic sites
- ❏ Restrooms
- ❏ Showers
- ❏ Trailer Access
- ❏ Visitor center
- ❏ Group Camping
- ❏ RV Camp
- ❏ Rustic Camping
- ❏ Cabins / Yurts
- ❏ Day Use Area

Notes:

Get the Facts

- ❏ Phone   731-253-9652
- ❏ Park Hours

  _____

- ❏ Reservations? ____Y ____N

  date made_____

- ❏ Open all year ____Y____N

  dates_____

- ❏ Check in time _____
- ❏ Check out time _____
- ❏ Pet friendly _____Y _____N
- ❏ Max RV length _____
- ❏ Distance from home

  miles: _____

  hours: _____

- ❏ Address_____

  _____

  _____

Fees:

- ❏ Day Use $ _____
- ❏ Camp Sites $ _____
- ❏ RV Sites $ _____
- ❏ Refund policy

  _____

  _____

  _____

Make It Personal

Trip dates:

The weather was: Sunny Cloudy Rainy Stormy Snowy Foggy Warm Cold

Why I went:

How I got there: (circle all that apply)   Plane   Train   Car   Bus   Bike   Hike   RV   MC

I went with:

We stayed in (space, cabin # etc):

Most relaxing day:

Something funny:

Someone we met:

Best story told:

The kids liked this:

The best food:

Games played:

Something disappointing:

Next time I'll do this differently:

Fort Pillow State Park
City: Henning   County: Lauderdale

Plan your trip: https://tnstateparks.com/parks/fort-pillow

Activities:

- ☐ Birding
- ☐ Biking
- ☐ Boating
- ☐ Caving
- ☐ Disc Golf / Golf
- ☐ Fishing
- ☐ Hiking
- ☐ Horseback Riding
- ☐ Hunting
- ☐ Interpretive Programs
- ☐ Mountain Biking
- ☐ Paddling
- ☐ Rock Climbing
- ☐ Swimming
- ☐ Waterfalls
- ☐ Water sports
- ☐ Wildlife Viewing
- ☐
- ☐
- ☐
- ☐
- ☐
- ☐
- ☐
- ☐
- ☐
- ☐
- ☐
- ☐

Facilities:

- ☐ ADA
- ☐ Picnic sites
- ☐ Restrooms
- ☐ Showers
- ☐ Trailer Access
- ☐ Visitor center
- ☐ Group Camping
- ☐ RV Camp
- ☐ Rustic Camping
- ☐ Cabins / Yurts
- ☐ Day Use Area

Notes:

Get the Facts

- ☐ Phone   731-738-5581
- ☐ Park Hours

  _____

- ☐ Reservations? ____Y ____N

  date made_____
- ☐ Open all year ____Y____N

  dates_____
- ☐ Check in time _____
- ☐ Check out time _____
- ☐ Pet friendly _____Y _____N
- ☐ Max RV length _____
- ☐ Distance from home

  miles: _____

  hours: _____
- ☐ Address_____

  _____

  _____

Fees:

- ☐ Day Use $ _____
- ☐ Camp Sites $ _____
- ☐ RV Sites $ _____
- ☐ Refund policy

  _____

  _____

  _____

Make It Personal

Trip dates: _____ | The weather was: Sunny Cloudy Rainy Stormy Snowy Foggy Warm Cold

Why I went:
_____

_____

How I got there: (circle all that apply)   Plane   Train   Car   Bus   Bike   Hike   RV   MC
_____

I went with:
_____

We stayed in (space, cabin # etc):
_____

Most relaxing day:
_____

_____

Something funny:
_____

_____

Someone we met:
_____

_____

Best story told:
_____

_____

The kids liked this:
_____

_____

The best food:
_____

_____

Games played:
_____

_____

Something disappointing:
_____

_____

Next time I'll do this differently:
_____

_____

T. O. Fuller State Park

City: Memphis   **County: Shelby**

Plan your trip: https://tnstateparks.com/parks/t-o-fuller

Activities:

- ❑ Birding
- ❑ Biking
- ❑ Boating
- ❑ Caving
- ❑ Disc Golf / Golf
- ❑ Fishing
- ❑ Hiking
- ❑ Horseback Riding
- ❑ Hunting
- ❑ Interpretive Programs

- ❑ Mountain Biking
- ❑ Paddling
- ❑ Rock Climbing
- ❑ Swimming
- ❑ Waterfalls
- ❑ Water sports
- ❑ Wildlife Viewing
- ❑
- ❑
- ❑
- ❑

- ❑
- ❑
- ❑
- ❑
- ❑
- ❑
- ❑
- ❑
- ❑
- ❑

Facilities:

- ❑ ADA
- ❑ Picnic sites
- ❑ Restrooms
- ❑ Showers
- ❑ Trailer Access
- ❑ Visitor center
- ❑ Group Camping
- ❑ RV Camp
- ❑ Rustic Camping
- ❑ Cabins / Yurts
- ❑ Day Use Area

Notes:

Get the Facts

- ❑ Phone   901-543-7581
- ❑ Park Hours

  _____

- ❑ Reservations? ____Y ____N

  date made_____

- ❑ Open all year ____Y____N

  dates_____

- ❑ Check in time _____
- ❑ Check out time _____
- ❑ Pet friendly _____Y _____N
- ❑ Max RV length _____
- ❑ Distance from home

  miles: _____

  hours: _____

- ❑ Address_____

  _____

  _____

Fees:

- ❑ Day Use $ _____
- ❑ Camp Sites $ _____
- ❑ RV Sites $ _____
- ❑ Refund policy

  _____

  _____

  _____

Make It Personal

Trip dates: _____ | The weather was: Sunny Cloudy Rainy Stormy Snowy Foggy Warm Cold

Why I went:
_____

_____

How I got there: (circle all that apply)   Plane   Train   Car   Bus   Bike   Hike   RV   MC
_____

I went with:
_____

We stayed in (space, cabin # etc):
_____

Most relaxing day:
_____

_____

Something funny:
_____

_____

Someone we met:
_____

_____

Best story told:
_____

_____

The kids liked this:
_____

_____

The best food:
_____

_____

Games played:
_____

_____

Something disappointing:
_____

_____

Next time I'll do this differently:
_____

_____

Meeman-Shelby Forest State Park
City: Millington　　　　County: Shelby

Plan your trip: https://tnstateparks.com/parks/meeman-shelby

Activities:

- ❑ Birding
- ❑ Biking
- ❑ Boating
- ❑ Caving
- ❑ Disc Golf / Golf
- ❑ Fishing
- ❑ Hiking
- ❑ Horseback Riding
- ❑ Hunting
- ❑ Interpretive Programs

- ❑ Mountain Biking
- ❑ Paddling
- ❑ Rock Climbing
- ❑ Swimming
- ❑ Waterfalls
- ❑ Water sports
- ❑ Wildlife Viewing
- ❑
- ❑
- ❑
- ❑

- ❑
- ❑
- ❑
- ❑
- ❑
- ❑
- ❑
- ❑
- ❑
- ❑
- ❑

Facilities:

- ❑ ADA
- ❑ Picnic sites
- ❑ Restrooms
- ❑ Showers
- ❑ Trailer Access
- ❑ Visitor center
- ❑ Group Camping
- ❑ RV Camp
- ❑ Rustic Camping
- ❑ Cabins / Yurts
- ❑ Day Use Area

Notes:

Get the Facts

- ❑ Phone　901-876-5215
- ❑ Park Hours

  _____

- ❑ Reservations? ____Y ____N

  date made_____

- ❑ Open all year ____Y_____N

  dates_____

- ❑ Check in time _____

- ❑ Check out time _____

- ❑ Pet friendly _____Y _____N

- ❑ Max RV length _____

- ❑ Distance from home

  miles: _____

  hours: _____

- ❑ Address_____

  _____

  _____

Fees:

- ❑ Day Use $ _____
- ❑ Camp Sites $ _____
- ❑ RV Sites $ _____
- ❑ Refund policy

  _____

  _____

  _____

Make It Personal

Trip dates:

The weather was: Sunny Cloudy Rainy Stormy Snowy Foggy Warm Cold

Why I went:

_____

How I got there: (circle all that apply)   Plane   Train   Car   Bus   Bike   Hike   RV   MC

I went with:

_____

We stayed in (space, cabin # etc):

_____

Most relaxing day:

_____

Something funny:

_____

Someone we met:

_____

Best story told:

_____

The kids liked this:

_____

The best food:

_____

Games played:

_____

Something disappointing:

_____

Next time I'll do this differently:

_____

_____

Siege and Battle of Corinth Sites
City: Pocahontas   County: Hardeman

Plan your trip: https://www.nps.gov/articles/the-siege-and-battle-of-corinth-a-new-kind-of-war-teaching-with-historic-places.htm

History:

Things To Do:

- ❑ ADA availability
- ❑ Public Restrooms
- ❑ Gift Shop
- ❑ Museum
- ❑ Visitor Center
- ❑ Picnic areas
- ❑ Chamber of Commerce
- ❑ Monuments
- ❑ Art Galleries
- ❑ Tours
- ❑ Street Art
- ❑ Natural Areas
- ❑ Living History
- ❑ Cemetery
- ❑ Amphitheater

Places I Want to Visit in the Area:

Restaurants:

Boutiques & Shops:

Monuments:

Museums:

Get the Facts

- ❑ Address_____
  _____
- ❑ Phone   202-208-6843
- ❑ Best season to visit
  _____
- ❑ Pet Friendly   Y   N
- ❑ Reservations?   Y   N
  date made_____
- ❑ Distance from home
  miles: _____
  hours: _____

Budget for this trip:

Parking	$
Food	$
Museums	$
Hotel	$
Shopping	$
Total	$

Notes:

Restaurant:

My Experience:

Shopping:

Best Find:

The shop I want to go back to:

Museum:

The coolest thing I learned about this area:

Other:

Shiloh Indian Mounds Site
City: Hurley   County: Hardin

Plan your trip: https://www.nps.gov/shil/moundshistory.htm

History:

Get the Facts

- ❑ Address_____
  _____
- ❑ Phone   731-689-5696
- ❑ Best season to visit
  _____
- ❑ Pet Friendly   Y   N
- ❑ Reservations?   Y   N
  date made_____
- ❑ Distance from home
  miles: _____
  hours: _____

Things To Do:

- ❑ ADA availability
- ❑ Public Restrooms
- ❑ Gift Shop
- ❑ Museum
- ❑ Visitor Center
- ❑ Picnic areas
- ❑ Chamber of Commerce
- ❑ Monuments
- ❑ Art Galleries
- ❑ Tours
- ❑ Street Art
- ❑ Natural Areas
- ❑ Living History
- ❑ Cemetery
- ❑ Amphitheater

Places I Want to Visit in the Area:

Restaurants:
Boutiques & Shops:
Monuments:
Museums:

Budget for this trip:

Parking	$
Food	$
Museums	$
Hotel	$
Shopping	$
Total	$

Notes:

Restaurant:

My Experience:

Shopping:

Best Find:

The shop I want to go back to:

Museum:

The coolest thing I learned about this area:

Other:

Collierville Historic District
City: Collierville   County: Shelby

Plan your trip: http://colliervilleparks.org/facilities-and-rental-information/greenbelt-trails-arboretum?showall=

History:

Get the Facts

❑ Address_____

_____

❑ Phone   901-457-2770

❑ Best season to visit

_____

❑ Pet Friendly   Y   N

❑ Reservations?   Y   N

date made_____

❑ Distance from home

miles: _____

hours: _____

Things To Do:

❑ ADA availability
❑ Public Restrooms
❑ Gift Shop
❑ Museum
❑ Visitor Center
❑ Picnic areas
❑ Chamber of Commerce

❑ Monuments
❑ Art Galleries
❑ Tours
❑ Street Art
❑ Natural Areas
❑ Living History
❑ Cemetery
❑ Amphitheater

Places I Want to Visit in the Area:

Restaurants:

Boutiques & Shops:

Monuments:

Museums:

Budget for this trip:

Parking	$
Food	$
Museums	$
Hotel	$
Shopping	$
Total	$

Notes:

Restaurant:

My Experience:

Shopping:

Best Find:

The shop I want to go back to:

Museum:

The coolest thing I learned about this area:

Other:

Beale Street Historic District

City: Memphis **County: Shelby**

Plan your trip: https://www.tnvacation.com/local/memphis-beale-street-historic-district

History:

Get the Facts

- ❏ Address_____

  _____

- ❏ Phone   901-526-0115
- ❏ Best season to visit

  _____

- ❏ Pet Friendly   Y   N
- ❏ Reservations?   Y   N

  date made_____

- ❏ Distance from home

  miles: _____

  hours: _____

Things To Do:

- ❏ ADA availability
- ❏ Public Restrooms
- ❏ Gift Shop
- ❏ Museum
- ❏ Visitor Center
- ❏ Picnic areas
- ❏ Chamber of Commerce
- ❏ Monuments
- ❏ Art Galleries
- ❏ Tours
- ❏ Street Art
- ❏ Natural Areas
- ❏ Living History
- ❏ Cemetery
- ❏ Amphitheater

Places I Want to Visit in the Area:

Restaurants:

Boutiques & Shops:

Monuments:

Museums:

Budget for this trip:

Parking	$
Food	$
Museums	$
Hotel	$
Shopping	$
Total	$

Notes:

Restaurant:

My Experience:

Shopping:

Best Find:

The shop I want to go back to:

Museum:

The coolest thing I learned about this area:

Other:

Chucalissa Archaeological Museum
City: Memphis   County: Shelby

Plan your trip: https://www.memphis.edu/chucalissa/

History:

Get the Facts

- ❑ Address_____

  _____

- ❑ Phone   901-785-3160
- ❑ Best season to visit

  _____

- ❑ Pet Friendly   Y   N
- ❑ Reservations?   Y   N

  date made_____

- ❑ Distance from home

  miles: _____

  hours: _____

Things To Do:

- ❑ ADA availability
- ❑ Public Restrooms
- ❑ Gift Shop
- ❑ Museum
- ❑ Visitor Center
- ❑ Picnic areas
- ❑ Chamber of Commerce
- ❑ Monuments
- ❑ Art Galleries
- ❑ Tours
- ❑ Street Art
- ❑ Natural Areas
- ❑ Living History
- ❑ Cemetery
- ❑ Amphitheater

Places I Want to Visit in the Area:

Restaurants:

Boutiques & Shops:

Monuments:

Museums:

Budget for this trip:

Parking	$
Food	$
Museums	$
Hotel	$
Shopping	$
Total	$

Notes:

Restaurant:

My Experience:

Shopping:

Best Find:

The shop I want to go back to:

Museum:

The coolest thing I learned about this area:

Other:

Cooper-Young Historic District
City: Memphis   County: Shelby

Plan your trip: https://cooperyoung.com/

History:

Get the Facts

- ❑ Address_____
  _____
- ❑ Phone   901-276-7222
- ❑ Best season to visit
  _____
- ❑ Pet Friendly   Y   N
- ❑ Reservations?   Y   N
  date made_____
- ❑ Distance from home
  miles: _____
  hours: _____

Things To Do:

- ❑ ADA availability
- ❑ Public Restrooms
- ❑ Gift Shop
- ❑ Museum
- ❑ Visitor Center
- ❑ Picnic areas
- ❑ Chamber of Commerce

- ❑ Monuments
- ❑ Art Galleries
- ❑ Tours
- ❑ Street Art
- ❑ Natural Areas
- ❑ Living History
- ❑ Cemetery
- ❑ Amphitheater

Places I Want to Visit in the Area:

Restaurants:

Boutiques & Shops:

Monuments:

Museums:

Budget for this trip:

Parking	$
Food	$
Museums	$
Hotel	$
Shopping	$
Total	$

Notes:

Restaurant:

My Experience:

Shopping:

Best Find:

The shop I want to go back to:

Museum:

The coolest thing I learned about this area:

Other:

Graceland (Home of Elvis Presley)
City: Memphis   County: Shelby

Plan your trip: https://www.graceland.com/

History:

Get the Facts

❑ Address_____

_____

❑ Phone   901-332-3322

❑ Best season to visit

_____

❑ Pet Friendly   Y   N

❑ Reservations?   Y   N

date made_____

❑ Distance from home

miles: _____

hours: _____

Things To Do:

❑ ADA availability
❑ Public Restrooms
❑ Gift Shop
❑ Museum
❑ Visitor Center
❑ Picnic areas
❑ Chamber of Commerce

❑ Monuments
❑ Art Galleries
❑ Tours
❑ Street Art
❑ Natural Areas
❑ Living History
❑ Cemetery
❑ Amphitheater

Budget for this trip:

Parking	$
Food	$
Museums	$
Hotel	$
Shopping	$
Total	$

Places I Want to Visit in the Area:

Restaurants:

Boutiques & Shops:

Monuments:

Museums:

Notes:

Restaurant:

My Experience:

Shopping:

Best Find:

The shop I want to go back to:

Museum:

The coolest thing I learned about this area:

Other:

Sun Record Company
City: Memphis   County: Shelby

Plan your trip: https://www.sunrecords.com/

History:

Things To Do:

- [ ] ADA availability
- [ ] Public Restrooms
- [ ] Gift Shop
- [ ] Museum
- [ ] Visitor Center
- [ ] Picnic areas
- [ ] Chamber of Commerce
- [ ] Monuments
- [ ] Art Galleries
- [ ] Tours
- [ ] Street Art
- [ ] Natural Areas
- [ ] Living History
- [ ] Cemetery
- [ ] Amphitheater

Places I Want to Visit in the Area:

Restaurants:

Boutiques & Shops:

Monuments:

Museums:

Get the Facts

- [ ] Address_____

_____

- [ ] Phone_____
- [ ] Best season to visit

_____

- [ ] Pet Friendly   Y   N
- [ ] Reservations? Y   N

date made_____

- [ ] Distance from home

miles: _____

hours: _____

Budget for this trip:

Parking	$
Food	$
Museums	$
Hotel	$
Shopping	$
Total	$

Notes:

Restaurant:

My Experience:

Shopping:

Best Find:

The shop I want to go back to:

Museum:

The coolest thing I learned about this area:

Other:

Pinson Mounds State Archaeological Park

City: Pinson **County: Madison**

Plan your trip: https://tnstateparks.com/parks/pinson-mounds

Activities:

- ❏ Biking
- ❏ Birding
- ❏ Boating
- ❏ Caving
- ❏ Disc Golf / Golf
- ❏ Fishing
- ❏ Hiking
- ❏ Hunting
- ❏ Paddling
- ❏ Rock Climbing
- ❏ Swimming
- ❏ Tours
- ❏ Watersports
- ❏ Wildlife Viewing
- ❏
- ❏
- ❏
- ❏
- ❏
- ❏
- ❏
- ❏
- ❏
- ❏

Facilities:

- ❏ ADA
- ❏ Gift Shop
- ❏ Museum
- ❏ Visitor Center
- ❏ Picnic sites
- ❏ Restrooms
- ❏
- ❏
- ❏
- ❏
- ❏
- ❏

Things to do in the area:

Get the Facts

- ❏ Phone 731-988-5614
- ❏ Park Hours

  _____

- ❏ Reservations? ____Y ____N

  date made_____

- ❏ Open all year? ____Y____N

  dates_____

- ❏ Dog friendly _____Y _____N

- ❏ Distance from home

  miles: _____

  hours: _____

- ❏ Address_____

  _____

  _____

Fees:

- ❏ Day Use $ _____
- ❏ Refund policy

  _____

  _____

  _____

Notes:

Riverbluff Walkway

City: Memphis   County: Shelby

Plan your trip: https://www.traillink.com/trail/riverbluff-walkway/

Activities:

- ❏ Biking
- ❏ Birding
- ❏ Boating
- ❏ Caving
- ❏ Disc Golf / Golf
- ❏ Fishing
- ❏ Hiking
- ❏ Hunting
- ❏ Paddling
- ❏ Rock Climbing
- ❏ Swimming
- ❏ Tours

- ❏ Watersports
- ❏ Wildlife Viewing
- ❏
- ❏
- ❏
- ❏
- ❏
- ❏
- ❏
- ❏
- ❏
- ❏

Facilities:

- ❏ ADA
- ❏ Gift Shop
- ❏ Museum
- ❏ Visitor Center
- ❏ Picnic sites
- ❏ Restrooms

- ❏
- ❏
- ❏
- ❏
- ❏
- ❏

Things to do in the area:

Get the Facts

- ❏ Phone 202-331-9696
- ❏ Park Hours

_____

- ❏ Reservations? ____Y ____N

  date made_____

- ❏ Open all year? ____Y____N

  dates_____

- ❏ Dog friendly ____Y ____N

- ❏ Distance from home

  miles: _____

  hours: _____

- ❏ Address_____

  _____

  _____

Fees:

- ❏ Day Use $ _____
- ❏ Refund policy

  _____
  _____
  _____

Notes:

Shelby Farms Park

City: Memphis   County: Shelby

Plan your trip: https://www.shelbyfarmspark.org/

Activities:

- ❏ Biking
- ❏ Birding
- ❏ Boating
- ❏ Caving
- ❏ Disc Golf / Golf
- ❏ Fishing
- ❏ Hiking
- ❏ Hunting
- ❏ Paddling
- ❏ Rock Climbing
- ❏ Swimming
- ❏ Tours

- ❏ Watersports
- ❏ Wildlife Viewing
- ❏
- ❏
- ❏
- ❏
- ❏
- ❏
- ❏
- ❏
- ❏
- ❏

Facilities:

- ❏ ADA
- ❏ Gift Shop
- ❏ Museum
- ❏ Visitor Center
- ❏ Picnic sites
- ❏ Restrooms

- ❏
- ❏
- ❏
- ❏
- ❏
- ❏

Things to do in the area:

Get the Facts

- ❏ Phone 901-222-7275
- ❏ Park Hours

  _____

- ❏ Reservations? _____Y _____N

  date made_____

- ❏ Open all year? _____Y_____N

  dates_____

- ❏ Dog friendly _____Y _____N

- ❏ Distance from home

  miles: _____

  hours: _____

- ❏ Address_____

  _____

  _____

Fees:

- ❏ Day Use $ _____
- ❏ Refund policy

  _____

  _____

  _____

Notes:

Big Cypress Tree State Park
City: Greenfield   County: Weakley

Plan your trip: https://tnstateparks.com/parks/big-cypress-tree

Activities:

- ❑ Biking
- ❑ Birding
- ❑ Boating
- ❑ Caving
- ❑ Disc Golf / Golf
- ❑ Fishing
- ❑ Hiking
- ❑ Hunting
- ❑ Paddling
- ❑ Rock Climbing
- ❑ Swimming
- ❑ Tours

- ❑ Watersports
- ❑ Wildlife Viewing
- ❑
- ❑
- ❑
- ❑
- ❑
- ❑
- ❑
- ❑
- ❑
- ❑

Facilities:

- ❑ ADA
- ❑ Gift Shop
- ❑ Museum
- ❑ Visitor Center
- ❑ Picnic sites
- ❑ Restrooms

- ❑
- ❑
- ❑
- ❑
- ❑
- ❑

Things to do in the area:

Get the Facts

- ❑ Phone 731-235-2700
- ❑ Park Hours

  _____

- ❑ Reservations? ____Y ____N

  date made_____

- ❑ Open all year? ____Y____N

  dates_____

- ❑ Dog friendly _____Y _____N

- ❑ Distance from home

  miles: _____

  hours: _____

- ❑ Address_____

  _____

  _____

Fees:

- ❑ Day Use $ _____
- ❑ Refund policy

  _____

  _____

  _____

Notes:

Tennessee State Park Trivia

1. What park had wintering Bald Eagles in the early 1970's when they were rarely observed in Tennessee?
A. Cove Lake State Park
B. Reelfoot Lake State Park
C. Radnor Lake State Natural Area

2. Which state park is built on a reclaimed strip mine?
A. Cumberland Mountain State Park
B. Roan Mountain State Park
C. Indian Mountain State Park

3. Which state park boasts the widest body of open water?
A. Paris Landing State Park
B. Mousetail Landing State Park
C. Pickwick Landing State Park

4. Which state park both a park boundary and a state boundary?
A. Red Clay State Historic Park
B. Rock Island State Park
C. Big Ridge State Park

5. Which state park has the most acreage?
A. Cumberland Mountain State Park
B. Justin P. Wilson Cumberland Trail SP
C. South Cumberland State Park

6. Which state park view is on Tennessee park rangers emblem?
A. Rugby Natural Area
B. Seven Islands State Birding Park
C. Cove Lake State Park

7. Which state park has the lowest elevation?
A. T. O. Fuller State Park
B. Panther Creek State Park
C. Tim's Ford State Park

8. What was the first area to become a state park?
A. Henry Horton State Park
B. Harrison Bay State Park
C. Harpeth River State Park

9. Which state park has no normal surface water in a lake or a stream?
A. Cedars of Lebanon State Park
B. Dunbar Cave State Park
C. Frozen Head State Park

10. Which state historic area preserves a site significant in the French and Indian War of 1754–1763?
A. Sgt. Alvin C. York State Historic Park
B. Johnsonville State Historic Park
C. Fort Loudoun State Historic Area

Key: 1=B, 2=C, 3=A 4=A, 5=C, 6=C, 7=A, 8=B, 9=A, 10=C

Middle Region

Long Hunter State Park
City: Hermitage   County: Davidson

Plan your trip: https://tnstateparks.com/parks/long-hunter

Activities:

- ☐ Birding
- ☐ Biking
- ☐ Boating
- ☐ Caving
- ☐ Disc Golf / Golf
- ☐ Fishing
- ☐ Hiking
- ☐ Horseback Riding
- ☐ Hunting
- ☐ Interpretive Programs
- ☐ Mountain Biking
- ☐ Paddling
- ☐ Rock Climbing
- ☐ Swimming
- ☐ Waterfalls
- ☐ Water sports
- ☐ Wildlife Viewing
- ☐
- ☐
- ☐
- ☐
- ☐
- ☐
- ☐
- ☐
- ☐
- ☐
- ☐
- ☐
- ☐
- ☐

Facilities:

- ☐ ADA
- ☐ Picnic sites
- ☐ Restrooms
- ☐ Showers
- ☐ Trailer Access
- ☐ Visitor center
- ☐ Group Camping
- ☐ RV Camp
- ☐ Rustic Camping
- ☐ Cabins / Yurts
- ☐ Day Use Area

Notes:

Get the Facts

- ☐ Phone   615-885-2422
- ☐ Park Hours

_____

- ☐ Reservations? ____Y ____N

date made_____

- ☐ Open all year ____Y____N

dates_____

- ☐ Check in time _____
- ☐ Check out time _____
- ☐ Pet friendly _____Y _____N
- ☐ Max RV length _____
- ☐ Distance from home

miles: _____

hours: _____

- ☐ Address_____

_____

_____

Fees:

- ☐ Day Use $ _____
- ☐ Camp Sites $ _____
- ☐ RV Sites $ _____
- ☐ Refund policy

_____

_____

_____

Make It Personal

Trip dates:

The weather was: Sunny Cloudy Rainy Stormy Snowy Foggy Warm Cold

Why I went:

How I got there: (circle all that apply) Plane Train Car Bus Bike Hike RV MC

I went with:

We stayed in (space, cabin # etc):

Most relaxing day:

Something funny:

Someone we met:

Best story told:

The kids liked this:

The best food:

Games played:

Something disappointing:

Next time I'll do this differently:

Natchez Trace Parkway
City: Nashville   County: Davidson

Plan your trip: https://tnstateparks.com/parks/natchez-trace

Activities:

- ❏ Birding
- ❏ Biking
- ❏ Boating
- ❏ Caving
- ❏ Disc Golf / Golf
- ❏ Fishing
- ❏ Hiking
- ❏ Horseback Riding
- ❏ Hunting
- ❏ Interpretive Programs
- ❏ Mountain Biking
- ❏ Paddling
- ❏ Rock Climbing
- ❏ Swimming
- ❏ Waterfalls
- ❏ Water sports
- ❏ Wildlife Viewing
- ❏
- ❏
- ❏
- ❏
- ❏
- ❏
- ❏
- ❏
- ❏
- ❏
- ❏
- ❏

Facilities:

- ❏ ADA
- ❏ Picnic sites
- ❏ Restrooms
- ❏ Showers
- ❏ Trailer Access
- ❏ Visitor center
- ❏ Group Camping
- ❏ RV Camp
- ❏ Rustic Camping
- ❏ Cabins / Yurts
- ❏ Day Use Area

Notes:

Get the Facts

- ❏ Phone   731-968-3742
- ❏ Park Hours

  _____

- ❏ Reservations? ____Y ____N

  date made_____
- ❏ Open all year ____Y____N

  dates_____
- ❏ Check in time _____
- ❏ Check out time _____
- ❏ Pet friendly _____Y _____N
- ❏ Max RV length _____
- ❏ Distance from home

  miles: _____

  hours: _____
- ❏ Address_____

  _____

  _____

Fees:

- ❏ Day Use $ _____
- ❏ Camp Sites $ _____
- ❏ RV Sites $ _____
- ❏ Refund policy

  _____

  _____

  _____

Make It Personal

Trip dates:

The weather was: Sunny Cloudy Rainy Stormy Snowy Foggy Warm Cold

Why I went:

How I got there: (circle all that apply) Plane Train Car Bus Bike Hike RV MC

I went with:

We stayed in (space, cabin # etc):

Most relaxing day:

Something funny:

Someone we met:

Best story told:

The kids liked this:

The best food:

Games played:

Something disappointing:

Next time I'll do this differently:

Montgomery Bell State Park
City: Burns   County: Dickson

Plan your trip: https://tnstateparks.com/parks/montgomery-bell

Activities:

- ❑ Birding
- ❑ Biking
- ❑ Boating
- ❑ Caving
- ❑ Disc Golf / Golf
- ❑ Fishing
- ❑ Hiking
- ❑ Horseback Riding
- ❑ Hunting
- ❑ Interpretive Programs
- ❑ Mountain Biking
- ❑ Paddling
- ❑ Rock Climbing
- ❑ Swimming
- ❑ Waterfalls
- ❑ Water sports
- ❑ Wildlife Viewing
- ❑
- ❑
- ❑
- ❑
- ❑
- ❑
- ❑
- ❑
- ❑
- ❑
- ❑
- ❑
- ❑
- ❑

Facilities:

- ❑ ADA
- ❑ Picnic sites
- ❑ Restrooms
- ❑ Showers
- ❑ Trailer Access
- ❑ Visitor center
- ❑ Group Camping
- ❑ RV Camp
- ❑ Rustic Camping
- ❑ Cabins / Yurts
- ❑ Day Use Area

Notes:

Get the Facts

- ❑ Phone   615-797-9052
- ❑ Park Hours

  _____

- ❑ Reservations? ____Y ____N

  date made_____

- ❑ Open all year ____Y____N

  dates_____

- ❑ Check in time _____

- ❑ Check out time _____

- ❑ Pet friendly _____Y _____N

- ❑ Max RV length _____

- ❑ Distance from home

  miles: _____

  hours: _____

- ❑ Address_____

  _____

  _____

Fees:

- ❑ Day Use $ _____
- ❑ Camp Sites $ _____
- ❑ RV Sites $ _____
- ❑ Refund policy

  _____

  _____

  _____

Make It Personal

Trip dates: _____ | The weather was: Sunny Cloudy Rainy Stormy Snowy Foggy Warm Cold

Why I went:
_____

_____

How I got there: (circle all that apply)   Plane   Train   Car   Bus   Bike   Hike   RV   MC
_____

I went with:
_____

We stayed in (space, cabin # etc):
_____

Most relaxing day:
_____

_____

Something funny:
_____

_____

Someone we met:
_____

_____

Best story told:
_____

_____

The kids liked this:
_____

_____

The best food:
_____

_____

Games played:
_____

_____

Something disappointing:
_____

_____

Next time I'll do this differently:
_____

_____

David Crockett State Park
City: Lawrenceburg   County: Lawrence

Plan your trip: https://tnstateparks.com/parks/david-crockett

Activities:

- ☐ Birding
- ☐ Biking
- ☐ Boating
- ☐ Caving
- ☐ Disc Golf / Golf
- ☐ Fishing
- ☐ Hiking
- ☐ Horseback Riding
- ☐ Hunting
- ☐ Interpretive Programs

- ☐ Mountain Biking
- ☐ Paddling
- ☐ Rock Climbing
- ☐ Swimming
- ☐ Waterfalls
- ☐ Water sports
- ☐ Wildlife Viewing
- ☐
- ☐
- ☐
- ☐

- ☐
- ☐
- ☐
- ☐
- ☐
- ☐
- ☐
- ☐
- ☐
- ☐
- ☐

Facilities:

- ☐ ADA
- ☐ Picnic sites
- ☐ Restrooms
- ☐ Showers
- ☐ Trailer Access
- ☐ Visitor center
- ☐ Group Camping
- ☐ RV Camp
- ☐ Rustic Camping
- ☐ Cabins / Yurts
- ☐ Day Use Area

Notes:

Get the Facts

- ☐ Phone   931-762-9408
- ☐ Park Hours

  _____

- ☐ Reservations? _____Y _____N

  date made_____

- ☐ Open all year _____Y_____N

  dates_____

- ☐ Check in time _____
- ☐ Check out time _____
- ☐ Pet friendly _____Y _____N
- ☐ Max RV length _____
- ☐ Distance from home

  miles: _____

  hours: _____

- ☐ Address_____

  _____

  _____

Fees:

- ☐ Day Use $ _____
- ☐ Camp Sites $ _____
- ☐ RV Sites $ _____
- ☐ Refund policy

  _____

  _____

  _____

Make It Personal

Trip dates:

The weather was: Sunny Cloudy Rainy Stormy Snowy Foggy Warm Cold

Why I went:

_____

How I got there: (circle all that apply) Plane Train Car Bus Bike Hike RV MC

I went with:

We stayed in (space, cabin # etc):

Most relaxing day:

_____

Something funny:

_____

Someone we met:

_____

Best story told:

_____

The kids liked this:

_____

The best food:

_____

Games played:

_____

Something disappointing:

_____

Next time I'll do this differently:

_____

_____

Henry Horton State Park
City: Chapel Hill   County: Marshall

Plan your trip: https://tnstateparks.com/parks/henry-horton

Activities:

- ❑ Birding
- ❑ Biking
- ❑ Boating
- ❑ Caving
- ❑ Disc Golf / Golf
- ❑ Fishing
- ❑ Hiking
- ❑ Horseback Riding
- ❑ Hunting
- ❑ Interpretive Programs

- ❑ Mountain Biking
- ❑ Paddling
- ❑ Rock Climbing
- ❑ Swimming
- ❑ Waterfalls
- ❑ Water sports
- ❑ Wildlife Viewing
- ❑
- ❑
- ❑
- ❑

- ❑
- ❑
- ❑
- ❑
- ❑
- ❑
- ❑
- ❑
- ❑
- ❑
- ❑

Facilities:

- ❑ ADA
- ❑ Picnic sites
- ❑ Restrooms
- ❑ Showers
- ❑ Trailer Access
- ❑ Visitor center
- ❑ Group Camping
- ❑ RV Camp
- ❑ Rustic Camping
- ❑ Cabins / Yurts
- ❑ Day Use Area

Notes:

Get the Facts

- ❑ Phone   931-364-2222
- ❑ Park Hours

  _____

- ❑ Reservations? ____Y ____N

  date made_____

- ❑ Open all year ____Y_____N

  dates_____

- ❑ Check in time _____
- ❑ Check out time _____
- ❑ Pet friendly _____Y _____N
- ❑ Max RV length _____
- ❑ Distance from home

  miles: _____

  hours: _____

- ❑ Address_____

  _____

  _____

Fees:

- ❑ Day Use $ _____
- ❑ Camp Sites $ _____
- ❑ RV Sites $ _____
- ❑ Refund policy

  _____

  _____

  _____

Make It Personal

Trip dates: _____ | The weather was: Sunny Cloudy Rainy Stormy Snowy Foggy Warm Cold

Why I went:
_____

_____

How I got there: (circle all that apply)   Plane   Train   Car   Bus   Bike   Hike   RV   MC

I went with:
_____

We stayed in (space, cabin # etc):
_____

Most relaxing day:
_____

Something funny:
_____

Someone we met:
_____

Best story told:
_____

The kids liked this:
_____

The best food:
_____

Games played:
_____

Something disappointing:
_____

Next time I'll do this differently:
_____

_____

Mousetail Landing State Park
City: Linden   County: Perry

Plan your trip: https://tnstateparks.com/parks/mousetail-landing

Activities:

- ❑ Birding
- ❑ Biking
- ❑ Boating
- ❑ Caving
- ❑ Disc Golf / Golf
- ❑ Fishing
- ❑ Hiking
- ❑ Horseback Riding
- ❑ Hunting
- ❑ Interpretive Programs

- ❑ Mountain Biking
- ❑ Paddling
- ❑ Rock Climbing
- ❑ Swimming
- ❑ Waterfalls
- ❑ Water sports
- ❑ Wildlife Viewing
- ❑
- ❑
- ❑
- ❑

- ❑
- ❑
- ❑
- ❑
- ❑
- ❑
- ❑
- ❑
- ❑
- ❑

Facilities:

- ❑ ADA
- ❑ Picnic sites
- ❑ Restrooms
- ❑ Showers
- ❑ Trailer Access
- ❑ Visitor center
- ❑ Group Camping
- ❑ RV Camp
- ❑ Rustic Camping
- ❑ Cabins / Yurts
- ❑ Day Use Area

Notes:

Get the Facts

- ❑ Phone   731-847-0841
- ❑ Park Hours

  _____

- ❑ Reservations? ____Y ____N

  date made_____
- ❑ Open all year ____Y____N

  dates_____
- ❑ Check in time _____
- ❑ Check out time _____
- ❑ Pet friendly _____Y _____N
- ❑ Max RV length _____
- ❑ Distance from home

  miles: _____

  hours: _____
- ❑ Address_____

  _____

  _____

Fees:

- ❑ Day Use $ _____
- ❑ Camp Sites $ _____
- ❑ RV Sites $ _____
- ❑ Refund policy

  _____

  _____

  _____

Make It Personal

Trip dates: _____ | The weather was: Sunny Cloudy Rainy Stormy Snowy Foggy Warm Cold

Why I went:
_____

How I got there: (circle all that apply)   Plane   Train   Car   Bus   Bike   Hike   RV   MC

I went with:
_____

We stayed in (space, cabin # etc):
_____

Most relaxing day:
_____

Something funny:
_____

Someone we met:
_____

Best story told:
_____

The kids liked this:
_____

The best food:
_____

Games played:
_____

Something disappointing:
_____

Next time I'll do this differently:
_____
_____

Bledsoe Creek State Park
City: Gallatin   County: Sumner

Plan your trip: https://tnstateparks.com/parks/bledsoe-creek

Activities:

- ❑ Birding
- ❑ Biking
- ❑ Boating
- ❑ Caving
- ❑ Disc Golf / Golf
- ❑ Fishing
- ❑ Hiking
- ❑ Horseback Riding
- ❑ Hunting
- ❑ Interpretive Programs

- ❑ Mountain Biking
- ❑ Paddling
- ❑ Rock Climbing
- ❑ Swimming
- ❑ Waterfalls
- ❑ Water sports
- ❑ Wildlife Viewing
- ❑
- ❑
- ❑
- ❑

- ❑
- ❑
- ❑
- ❑
- ❑
- ❑
- ❑
- ❑
- ❑
- ❑
- ❑

Facilities:

- ❑ ADA
- ❑ Picnic sites
- ❑ Restrooms
- ❑ Showers
- ❑ Trailer Access
- ❑ Visitor center
- ❑ Group Camping
- ❑ RV Camp
- ❑ Rustic Camping
- ❑ Cabins / Yurts
- ❑ Day Use Area

Notes:

Get the Facts

- ❑ Phone   615-452-3706
- ❑ Park Hours

  _____

- ❑ Reservations? ____ Y ____ N

  date made_____

- ❑ Open all year ____ Y ____ N

  dates_____

- ❑ Check in time _____

- ❑ Check out time _____

- ❑ Pet friendly _____ Y _____ N

- ❑ Max RV length _____

- ❑ Distance from home

  miles: _____

  hours: _____

- ❑ Address_____

  _____

  _____

Fees:

- ❑ Day Use $ _____
- ❑ Camp Sites $ _____
- ❑ RV Sites $ _____
- ❑ Refund policy

  _____

  _____

  _____

Make It Personal

Trip dates:

The weather was: Sunny Cloudy Rainy Stormy Snowy Foggy Warm Cold

Why I went:

_____

How I got there: (circle all that apply) Plane Train Car Bus Bike Hike RV MC

I went with:

We stayed in (space, cabin # etc):

Most relaxing day:

_____

Something funny:

_____

Someone we met:

_____

Best story told:

_____

The kids liked this:

_____

The best food:

_____

Games played:

_____

Something disappointing:

_____

Next time I'll do this differently:

_____

Cedars of Lebanon State Park

City: Lebanon   County: Wilson

Plan your trip: https://tnstateparks.com/parks/cedars-of-lebanon

Activities:

- ❑ Birding
- ❑ Biking
- ❑ Boating
- ❑ Caving
- ❑ Disc Golf / Golf
- ❑ Fishing
- ❑ Hiking
- ❑ Horseback Riding
- ❑ Hunting
- ❑ Interpretive Programs

- ❑ Mountain Biking
- ❑ Paddling
- ❑ Rock Climbing
- ❑ Swimming
- ❑ Waterfalls
- ❑ Water sports
- ❑ Wildlife Viewing
- ❑
- ❑
- ❑
- ❑

- ❑
- ❑
- ❑
- ❑
- ❑
- ❑
- ❑
- ❑
- ❑
- ❑
- ❑

Facilities:

- ❑ ADA
- ❑ Picnic sites
- ❑ Restrooms
- ❑ Showers
- ❑ Trailer Access
- ❑ Visitor center
- ❑ Group Camping
- ❑ RV Camp
- ❑ Rustic Camping
- ❑ Cabins / Yurts
- ❑ Day Use Area

Notes:

Get the Facts

- ❑ Phone   615-443-2769
- ❑ Park Hours

  _____

- ❑ Reservations? _____Y _____N

  date made_____

- ❑ Open all year _____Y_____N

  dates_____

- ❑ Check in time _____
- ❑ Check out time _____
- ❑ Pet friendly _____Y _____N
- ❑ Max RV length _____
- ❑ Distance from home

  miles: _____

  hours: _____

- ❑ Address_____

  _____

  _____

Fees:

- ❑ Day Use $ _____
- ❑ Camp Sites $ _____
- ❑ RV Sites $ _____
- ❑ Refund policy

  _____

  _____

  _____

Make It Personal

Trip dates: _____

The weather was: Sunny Cloudy Rainy Stormy Snowy Foggy Warm Cold

Why I went:

_____

How I got there: (circle all that apply)   Plane   Train   Car   Bus   Bike   Hike   RV   MC

I went with:

_____

We stayed in (space, cabin # etc):

_____

Most relaxing day:

_____

Something funny:

_____

Someone we met:

_____

Best story told:

_____

The kids liked this:

_____

The best food:

_____

Games played:

_____

Something disappointing:

_____

Next time I'll do this differently:

_____

Montgomery Bell Tunnel
City: Kingston Springs   County: Cheatham

Plan your trip: https://www.atlasobscura.com/places/montgomery-bell-tunnel

History:

Get the Facts

- ❑ Address_____
  _____
- ❑ Phone
- ❑ Best season to visit
  _____
- ❑ Pet Friendly   Y   N
- ❑ Reservations?   Y   N
  date made_____
- ❑ Distance from home
  miles: _____
  hours: _____

Things To Do:

- ❑ ADA availability
- ❑ Public Restrooms
- ❑ Gift Shop
- ❑ Museum
- ❑ Visitor Center
- ❑ Picnic areas
- ❑ Chamber of Commerce
- ❑ Monuments
- ❑ Art Galleries
- ❑ Tours
- ❑ Street Art
- ❑ Natural Areas
- ❑ Living History
- ❑ Cemetery
- ❑ Amphitheater

Places I Want to Visit in the Area:

Restaurants:

Boutiques & Shops:

Monuments:

Museums:

Budget for this trip:

Parking	$
Food	$
Museums	$
Hotel	$
Shopping	$
Total	$

Notes:

Restaurant:

My Experience:

Shopping:

Best Find:

The shop I want to go back to:

Museum:

The coolest thing I learned about this area:

Other:

George Peabody College for Teachers

City: Nashville   **County: Davidson**

Plan your trip: https://peabody.vanderbilt.edu/

History:

Things To Do:

- ❑ ADA availability
- ❑ Public Restrooms
- ❑ Gift Shop
- ❑ Museum
- ❑ Visitor Center
- ❑ Picnic areas
- ❑ Chamber of Commerce
- ❑ Monuments
- ❑ Art Galleries
- ❑ Tours
- ❑ Street Art
- ❑ Natural Areas
- ❑ Living History
- ❑ Cemetery
- ❑ Amphitheater

Places I Want to Visit in the Area:

Restaurants:

Boutiques & Shops:

Monuments:

Museums:

Get the Facts

- ❑ Address_____
  _____
- ❑ Phone 615-322-8407
- ❑ Best season to visit
  _____
- ❑ Pet Friendly   Y   N
- ❑ Reservations?   Y   N
  date made_____
- ❑ Distance from home
  miles: _____
  hours: _____

Budget for this trip:

Parking	$
Food	$
Museums	$
Hotel	$
Shopping	$
Total	$

Notes:

Restaurant:

My Experience:

Shopping:

Best Find:

The shop I want to go back to:

Museum:

The coolest thing I learned about this area:

Other:

Hermitage Hotel
City: Nashville   County: Davidson
Plan your trip: https://www.thehermitagehotel.com/

History:

Things To Do:

- ❑ ADA availability
- ❑ Public Restrooms
- ❑ Gift Shop
- ❑ Museum
- ❑ Visitor Center
- ❑ Picnic areas
- ❑ Chamber of Commerce
- ❑ Monuments
- ❑ Art Galleries
- ❑ Tours
- ❑ Street Art
- ❑ Natural Areas
- ❑ Living History
- ❑ Cemetery
- ❑ Amphitheater

Places I Want to Visit in the Area:

Restaurants:
Boutiques & Shops:
Monuments:
Museums:

Get the Facts

- ❑ Address_____
  _____
- ❑ Phone   888-888-9414
- ❑ Best season to visit
  _____
- ❑ Pet Friendly   Y   N
- ❑ Reservations?   Y   N
  date made_____
- ❑ Distance from home
  miles: _____
  hours: _____

Budget for this trip:

Parking	$
Food	$
Museums	$
Hotel	$
Shopping	$
Total	$

Notes:

Restaurant:

My Experience:

Shopping:

Best Find:

The shop I want to go back to:

Museum:

The coolest thing I learned about this area:

Other:

Jubilee Hall at Fisk University
City: Nashville   County: Davidson

Plan your trip: https://www.fisk.edu/about/history/#

History:

Get the Facts

- ❏ Address_____

  _____

- ❏ Phone 615-329-8735
- ❏ Best season to visit

  _____

- ❏ Pet Friendly   Y   N
- ❏ Reservations?   Y   N

  date made_____

- ❏ Distance from home

  miles: _____

  hours: _____

Things To Do:

- ❏ ADA availability
- ❏ Public Restrooms
- ❏ Gift Shop
- ❏ Museum
- ❏ Visitor Center
- ❏ Picnic areas
- ❏ Chamber of Commerce

- ❏ Monuments
- ❏ Art Galleries
- ❏ Tours
- ❏ Street Art
- ❏ Natural Areas
- ❏ Living History
- ❏ Cemetery
- ❏ Amphitheater

Budget for this trip:

Parking	$
Food	$
Museums	$
Hotel	$
Shopping	$
Total	$

Places I Want to Visit in the Area:

Restaurants:

Boutiques & Shops:

Monuments:

Museums:

Notes:

Restaurant:

My Experience:

Shopping:

Best Find:

The shop I want to go back to:

Museum:

The coolest thing I learned about this area:

Other:

Music Row
City: Nashville   County: Davidson
Plan your trip: https://www.trolleytours.com/nashville/music-row

History:

Get the Facts
- ❑ Address_____
  _____
- ❑ Phone   615-375-3166
- ❑ Best season to visit
  _____
- ❑ Pet Friendly   Y   N
- ❑ Reservations?   Y   N
  date made_____
- ❑ Distance from home
  miles: _____
  hours: _____

Things To Do:
- ❑ ADA availability
- ❑ Public Restrooms
- ❑ Gift Shop
- ❑ Museum
- ❑ Visitor Center
- ❑ Picnic areas
- ❑ Chamber of Commerce
- ❑ Monuments
- ❑ Art Galleries
- ❑ Tours
- ❑ Street Art
- ❑ Natural Areas
- ❑ Living History
- ❑ Cemetery
- ❑ Amphitheater

Places I Want to Visit in the Area:

Restaurants:

Boutiques & Shops:

Monuments:

Museums:

Budget for this trip:

Parking	$
Food	$
Museums	$
Hotel	$
Shopping	$
Total	$

Notes:

Restaurant:

My Experience:

Shopping:

Best Find:

The shop I want to go back to:

Museum:

The coolest thing I learned about this area:

Other:

Old First Presbyterian Church
City: Nashville   County: Davidson

Plan your trip: https://www.fpcknox.org/about/history/church-history/

History:

Get the Facts

- ❑ Address_____
  _____
- ❑ Phone 865-546-2531
- ❑ Best season to visit
  _____
- ❑ Pet Friendly   Y   N
- ❑ Reservations?   Y   N
  date made_____
- ❑ Distance from home
  miles: _____
  hours: _____

Things To Do:

- ❑ ADA availability
- ❑ Public Restrooms
- ❑ Gift Shop
- ❑ Museum
- ❑ Visitor Center
- ❑ Picnic areas
- ❑ Chamber of Commerce
- ❑ Monuments
- ❑ Art Galleries
- ❑ Tours
- ❑ Street Art
- ❑ Natural Areas
- ❑ Living History
- ❑ Cemetery
- ❑ Amphitheater

Places I Want to Visit in the Area:

Restaurants:

Boutiques & Shops:

Monuments:

Museums:

Budget for this trip:

Parking	$
Food	$
Museums	$
Hotel	$
Shopping	$
Total	$

Notes:

Restaurant:

My Experience:

Shopping:

Best Find:

The shop I want to go back to:

Museum:

The coolest thing I learned about this area:

Other:

Ryman Auditorium

City: Nashville   County: Davidson

Plan your trip: https://ryman.com/

History:

Get the Facts

- ❑ Address_____

  _____

- ❑ Phone   615-458-8700
- ❑ Best season to visit

  _____

- ❑ Pet Friendly   Y   N
- ❑ Reservations?   Y   N

  date made_____

- ❑ Distance from home

  miles: _____

  hours: _____

Things To Do:

- ❑ ADA availability
- ❑ Public Restrooms
- ❑ Gift Shop
- ❑ Museum
- ❑ Visitor Center
- ❑ Picnic areas
- ❑ Chamber of Commerce
- ❑ Monuments
- ❑ Art Galleries
- ❑ Tours
- ❑ Street Art
- ❑ Natural Areas
- ❑ Living History
- ❑ Cemetery
- ❑ Amphitheater

Places I Want to Visit in the Area:

Restaurants:
Boutiques & Shops:
Monuments:
Museums:

Budget for this trip:

Parking	$
Food	$
Museums	$
Hotel	$
Shopping	$
Total	$

Notes:

Restaurant:

My Experience:

Shopping:

Best Find:

The shop I want to go back to:

Museum:

The coolest thing I learned about this area:

Other:

Tennessee State Capitol
City: Nashville   County: Davidson

Plan your trip: https://tnmuseum.org/state-capitol

History:

Things To Do:

- ❑ ADA availability
- ❑ Public Restrooms
- ❑ Gift Shop
- ❑ Museum
- ❑ Visitor Center
- ❑ Picnic areas
- ❑ Chamber of Commerce
- ❑ Monuments
- ❑ Art Galleries
- ❑ Tours
- ❑ Street Art
- ❑ Natural Areas
- ❑ Living History
- ❑ Cemetery
- ❑ Amphitheater

Places I Want to Visit in the Area:

Restaurants:

Boutiques & Shops:

Monuments:

Museums:

Get the Facts

- ❑ Address_____
  _____
- ❑ Phone 615-741-2692
- ❑ Best season to visit
  _____
- ❑ Pet Friendly   Y   N
- ❑ Reservations?   Y   N
  date made_____
- ❑ Distance from home
  miles: _____
  hours: _____

Budget for this trip:

Parking	$
Food	$
Museums	$
Hotel	$
Shopping	$
Total	$

Notes:

Restaurant:

My Experience:

Shopping:

Best Find:

The shop I want to go back to:

Museum:

The coolest thing I learned about this area:

Other:

The Hermitage

City: Nashville — County: Davidson

Plan your trip: https://thehermitage.com/

History:

Get the Facts

- ❑ Address_____

  _____

- ❑ Phone 615-889-2941
- ❑ Best season to visit

  _____

- ❑ Pet Friendly   Y   N
- ❑ Reservations?   Y   N

  date made_____

- ❑ Distance from home

  miles: _____

  hours: _____

Things To Do:

- ❑ ADA availability
- ❑ Public Restrooms
- ❑ Gift Shop
- ❑ Museum
- ❑ Visitor Center
- ❑ Picnic areas
- ❑ Chamber of Commerce
- ❑ Monuments
- ❑ Art Galleries
- ❑ Tours
- ❑ Street Art
- ❑ Natural Areas
- ❑ Living History
- ❑ Cemetery
- ❑ Amphitheater

Places I Want to Visit in the Area:

Restaurants:

Boutiques & Shops:

Monuments:

Museums:

Budget for this trip:

Parking	$
Food	$
Museums	$
Hotel	$
Shopping	$
Total	$

Notes:

Restaurant:

My Experience:

Shopping:

Best Find:

The shop I want to go back to:

Museum:

The coolest thing I learned about this area:

Other:

James K. Polk Home
City: Columbia   County: Maury

Plan your trip: https://jameskpolk.com/

History:

Things To Do:

- ❑ ADA availability
- ❑ Public Restrooms
- ❑ Gift Shop
- ❑ Museum
- ❑ Visitor Center
- ❑ Picnic areas
- ❑ Chamber of Commerce
- ❑ Monuments
- ❑ Art Galleries
- ❑ Tours
- ❑ Street Art
- ❑ Natural Areas
- ❑ Living History
- ❑ Cemetery
- ❑ Amphitheater

Places I Want to Visit in the Area:

Restaurants:
Boutiques & Shops:
Monuments:
Museums:

Get the Facts

- ❑ Address_____
  _____
- ❑ Phone 931-388-2354
- ❑ Best season to visit
  _____
- ❑ Pet Friendly   Y   N
- ❑ Reservations?   Y   N
  date made_____
- ❑ Distance from home
  miles: _____
  hours: _____

Budget for this trip:

Parking	$
Food	$
Museums	$
Hotel	$
Shopping	$
Total	$

Notes:

Restaurant:

My Experience:

Shopping:

Best Find:

The shop I want to go back to:

Museum:

The coolest thing I learned about this area:

Other:

Rattle and Snap Plantation
City: Columbia   County: Maury

Plan your trip: http://www.rattleandsnapplantation.com/

History:

Things To Do:

- ❑ ADA availability
- ❑ Public Restrooms
- ❑ Gift Shop
- ❑ Museum
- ❑ Visitor Center
- ❑ Picnic areas
- ❑ Chamber of Commerce
- ❑ Monuments
- ❑ Art Galleries
- ❑ Tours
- ❑ Street Art
- ❑ Natural Areas
- ❑ Living History
- ❑ Cemetery
- ❑ Amphitheater

Places I Want to Visit in the Area:

Restaurants:
Boutiques & Shops:
Monuments:
Museums:

Get the Facts

- ❑ Address_____
_____
- ❑ Phone   931-379-1700
- ❑ Best season to visit
_____
- ❑ Pet Friendly   Y   N
- ❑ Reservations?   Y   N
  date made_____
- ❑ Distance from home
  miles: _____
  hours: _____

Budget for this trip:

Parking	$
Food	$
Museums	$
Hotel	$
Shopping	$
Total	$

Notes:

Restaurant:

My Experience:

Shopping:

Best Find:

The shop I want to go back to:

Museum:

The coolest thing I learned about this area:

Other:

Sam Davis Home
City: Smyrna   County: Rutherford
Plan your trip: https://www.samdavishome.org/

History:

Things To Do:

- ☐ ADA availability
- ☐ Public Restrooms
- ☐ Gift Shop
- ☐ Museum
- ☐ Visitor Center
- ☐ Picnic areas
- ☐ Chamber of Commerce
- ☐ Monuments
- ☐ Art Galleries
- ☐ Tours
- ☐ Street Art
- ☐ Natural Areas
- ☐ Living History
- ☐ Cemetery
- ☐ Amphitheater

Places I Want to Visit in the Area:

Restaurants:
Boutiques & Shops:
Monuments:
Museums:

Get the Facts

- ☐ Address_____
  _____
- ☐ Phone 615-459-2341
- ☐ Best season to visit
  _____
- ☐ Pet Friendly Y N
- ☐ Reservations? Y N
  date made_____
- ☐ Distance from home
  miles: _____
  hours: _____

Budget for this trip:

Parking	$
Food	$
Museums	$
Hotel	$
Shopping	$
Total	$

Notes:

Restaurant:

My Experience:

Shopping:

Best Find:

The shop I want to go back to:

Museum:

The coolest thing I learned about this area:

Other:

Wynnewood State Historic Site
City: Castalian Springs   County: Sumner

Plan your trip: https://visitsumnertn.com/place/wynnewood-state-historic-site/

History:

Get the Facts

- ❑ Address_____

  _____

- ❑ Phone   615-452-7070
- ❑ Best season to visit

  _____

- ❑ Pet Friendly   Y   N
- ❑ Reservations?   Y   N

  date made_____

- ❑ Distance from home

  miles: _____

  hours: _____

Things To Do:

- ❑ ADA availability
- ❑ Public Restrooms
- ❑ Gift Shop
- ❑ Museum
- ❑ Visitor Center
- ❑ Picnic areas
- ❑ Chamber of Commerce
- ❑ Monuments
- ❑ Art Galleries
- ❑ Tours
- ❑ Street Art
- ❑ Natural Areas
- ❑ Living History
- ❑ Cemetery
- ❑ Amphitheater

Places I Want to Visit in the Area:

Restaurants:
Boutiques & Shops:
Monuments:
Museums:

Budget for this trip:

Parking	$
Food	$
Museums	$
Hotel	$
Shopping	$
Total	$

Notes:

Restaurant:

My Experience:

Shopping:

Best Find:

The shop I want to go back to:

Museum:

The coolest thing I learned about this area:

Other:

Franklin Battlefield
City: Franklin   County: Williamson

Plan your trip: https://tnstateparks.com/blog/a-weekend-at-pickett-ccc-memorial-state-park

History:

Things To Do:

- ❑ ADA availability
- ❑ Public Restrooms
- ❑ Gift Shop
- ❑ Museum
- ❑ Visitor Center
- ❑ Picnic areas
- ❑ Chamber of Commerce
- ❑ Monuments
- ❑ Art Galleries
- ❑ Tours
- ❑ Street Art
- ❑ Natural Areas
- ❑ Living History
- ❑ Cemetery
- ❑ Amphitheater

Places I Want to Visit in the Area:

Restaurants:
Boutiques & Shops:
Monuments:
Museums:

Get the Facts

- ❑ Address_____
  _____
- ❑ Phone   931-879-5821
- ❑ Best season to visit
  _____
- ❑ Pet Friendly   Y   N
- ❑ Reservations?   Y   N
  date made_____
- ❑ Distance from home
  miles: _____
  hours: _____

Budget for this trip:

Parking	$
Food	$
Museums	$
Hotel	$
Shopping	$
Total	$

Notes:

Restaurant:

My Experience:

Shopping:

Best Find:

The shop I want to go back to:

Museum:

The coolest thing I learned about this area:

Other:

Hiram Masonic Lodge No. 7
City: Franklin   County: Williamson

Plan your trip: https://www.tnvacation.com/civil-war/place/3454/hiram-masonic-lodge-no-7/

History:

Things To Do:

- ☐ ADA availability
- ☐ Public Restrooms
- ☐ Gift Shop
- ☐ Museum
- ☐ Visitor Center
- ☐ Picnic areas
- ☐ Chamber of Commerce
- ☐ Monuments
- ☐ Art Galleries
- ☐ Tours
- ☐ Street Art
- ☐ Natural Areas
- ☐ Living History
- ☐ Cemetery
- ☐ Amphitheater

Places I Want to Visit in the Area:

Restaurants:

Boutiques & Shops:

Monuments:

Museums:

Get the Facts

- ☐ Address_____

  _____

- ☐ Phone 615-790-1688
- ☐ Best season to visit

  _____

- ☐ Pet Friendly   Y   N
- ☐ Reservations?   Y   N

  date made_____

- ☐ Distance from home

  miles: _____

  hours: _____

Budget for this trip:

Parking	$
Food	$
Museums	$
Hotel	$
Shopping	$
Total	$

Notes:

Restaurant:

My Experience:

Shopping:

Best Find:

The shop I want to go back to:

Museum:

The coolest thing I learned about this area:

Other:

Downtown Franklin
City: Franklin   County: Williamson

Plan your trip: https://www.franklintn.gov/government/departments-k-z/parks/parks-amenities/greenways-trails

History:

Things To Do:

- [ ] ADA availability
- [ ] Public Restrooms
- [ ] Gift Shop
- [ ] Museum
- [ ] Visitor Center
- [ ] Picnic areas
- [ ] Chamber of Commerce
- [ ] Monuments
- [ ] Art Galleries
- [ ] Tours
- [ ] Street Art
- [ ] Natural Areas
- [ ] Living History
- [ ] Cemetery
- [ ] Amphitheater

Places I Want to Visit in the Area:

Restaurants:

Boutiques & Shops:

Monuments:

Museums:

Get the Facts

- [ ] Address_____
  _____
- [ ] Phone 615-791-3217
- [ ] Best season to visit
  _____
- [ ] Pet Friendly   Y   N
- [ ] Reservations?   Y   N
  date made_____
- [ ] Distance from home
  miles: _____
  hours: _____

Budget for this trip:

Parking	$
Food	$
Museums	$
Hotel	$
Shopping	$
Total	$

Notes:

Restaurant:

My Experience:

Shopping:

Best Find:

The shop I want to go back to:

Museum:

The coolest thing I learned about this area:

Other:

Harpeth River State Park
City: Kingston Springs   County: Cheatham

Plan your trip: https://tnstateparks.com/parks/harpeth-river

Activities:

- ❑ Biking
- ❑ Birding
- ❑ Boating
- ❑ Caving
- ❑ Disc Golf / Golf
- ❑ Fishing
- ❑ Hiking
- ❑ Hunting
- ❑ Paddling
- ❑ Rock Climbing
- ❑ Swimming
- ❑ Tours

- ❑ Watersports
- ❑ Wildlife Viewing
- ❑
- ❑
- ❑
- ❑
- ❑
- ❑
- ❑
- ❑
- ❑
- ❑

Facilities:

- ❑ ADA
- ❑ Gift Shop
- ❑ Museum
- ❑ Visitor Center
- ❑ Picnic sites
- ❑ Restrooms

- ❑
- ❑
- ❑
- ❑
- ❑
- ❑

Things to do in the area:

Get the Facts

- ❑ Phone 615-952-2099
- ❑ Park Hours

_____

- ❑ Reservations? ____Y ____N

date made_____

- ❑ Open all year? ____Y____N

dates_____

- ❑ Dog friendly _____Y _____N

- ❑ Distance from home

miles: _____

hours: _____

- ❑ Address_____

_____

_____

Fees:

- ❑ Day Use $ _____
- ❑ Refund policy

_____

_____

_____

Notes:

Bicentennial Capitol Mall State Park
City: Nashville   County: Davidson

Plan your trip: https://tnstateparks.com/parks/bicentennial-mall

Activities:

- ❑ Biking
- ❑ Birding
- ❑ Boating
- ❑ Caving
- ❑ Disc Golf / Golf
- ❑ Fishing
- ❑ Hiking
- ❑ Hunting
- ❑ Paddling
- ❑ Rock Climbing
- ❑ Swimming
- ❑ Tours

- ❑ Watersports
- ❑ Wildlife Viewing
- ❑
- ❑
- ❑
- ❑
- ❑
- ❑
- ❑
- ❑
- ❑
- ❑

Facilities:

- ❑ ADA
- ❑ Gift Shop
- ❑ Museum
- ❑ Visitor Center
- ❑ Picnic sites
- ❑ Restrooms

- ❑
- ❑
- ❑
- ❑
- ❑
- ❑

Things to do in the area:

Get the Facts

- ❑ Phone 615-741-5280
- ❑ Park Hours

_____

- ❑ Reservations? ____Y ____N

  date made_____

- ❑ Open all year? ____Y____N

  dates_____

- ❑ Dog friendly _____Y _____N
- ❑ Distance from home

  miles: _____

  hours: _____

- ❑ Address_____

  _____

  _____

Fees:

- ❑ Day Use $ _____
- ❑ Refund policy

  _____

  _____

  _____

Notes:

Radnor Lake State Natural Area
City: Nashville   County: Davidson

Plan your trip: https://tnstateparks.com/parks/radnor-lake

Activities:

- ❑ Biking
- ❑ Birding
- ❑ Boating
- ❑ Caving
- ❑ Disc Golf / Golf
- ❑ Fishing
- ❑ Hiking
- ❑ Hunting
- ❑ Paddling
- ❑ Rock Climbing
- ❑ Swimming
- ❑ Tours

- ❑ Watersports
- ❑ Wildlife Viewing
- ❑
- ❑
- ❑
- ❑
- ❑
- ❑
- ❑
- ❑
- ❑
- ❑

Facilities:

- ❑ ADA
- ❑ Gift Shop
- ❑ Museum
- ❑ Visitor Center
- ❑ Picnic sites
- ❑ Restrooms

- ❑
- ❑
- ❑
- ❑
- ❑
- ❑

Things to do in the area:

Get the Facts

- ❑ Phone 615-373-3467
- ❑ Park Hours

  _____

- ❑ Reservations? ____Y ____N

  date made_____

- ❑ Open all year? ____Y____N

  dates_____

- ❑ Dog friendly _____Y _____N

- ❑ Distance from home

  miles: _____

  hours: _____

- ❑ Address_____

  _____

  _____

Fees:

- ❑ Day Use $ _____
- ❑ Refund policy

  _____

  _____

  _____

Notes:

Johnsonville State Historic Park
City: New Johnsonville   County: Humphreys

Plan your trip: https://tnstateparks.com/parks/johnsonville

Activities:

- ❑ Biking
- ❑ Birding
- ❑ Boating
- ❑ Caving
- ❑ Disc Golf / Golf
- ❑ Fishing
- ❑ Hiking
- ❑ Hunting
- ❑ Paddling
- ❑ Rock Climbing
- ❑ Swimming
- ❑ Tours

- ❑ Watersports
- ❑ Wildlife Viewing
- ❑
- ❑
- ❑
- ❑
- ❑
- ❑
- ❑
- ❑
- ❑
- ❑

Facilities:

- ❑ ADA
- ❑ Gift Shop
- ❑ Museum
- ❑ Visitor Center
- ❑ Picnic sites
- ❑ Restrooms

- ❑
- ❑
- ❑
- ❑
- ❑
- ❑

Things to do in the area:

Get the Facts

- ❑ Phone 931-535-2789
- ❑ Park Hours

  _____

- ❑ Reservations? ____Y ____N

  date made_____

- ❑ Open all year? ____Y____N

  dates_____

- ❑ Dog friendly _____Y _____N

- ❑ Distance from home

  miles: _____

  hours: _____

- ❑ Address_____

  _____

  _____

Fees:

- ❑ Day Use $ _____
- ❑ Refund policy

  _____
  _____
  _____

Notes:

Dunbar Cave State Park
City: Clarksville   County: Montgomery

Plan your trip: https://tnstateparks.com/parks/dunbar-cave

Activities:

❑ Biking	❑ Watersports
❑ Birding	❑ Wildlife Viewing
❑ Boating	❑
❑ Caving	❑
❑ Disc Golf / Golf	❑
❑ Fishing	❑
❑ Hiking	❑
❑ Hunting	❑
❑ Paddling	❑
❑ Rock Climbing	❑
❑ Swimming	❑
❑ Tours	❑

Facilities:

❑ ADA	❑
❑ Gift Shop	❑
❑ Museum	❑
❑ Visitor Center	❑
❑ Picnic sites	❑
❑ Restrooms	❑

Things to do in the area:

Get the Facts

❑ Phone 931-648-5526

❑ Park Hours

_____

❑ Reservations? ____Y ____N

date made_____

❑ Open all year? ____Y____N

dates_____

❑ Dog friendly _____Y _____N

❑ Distance from home

miles: _____

hours: _____

❑ Address_____

_____

_____

Fees:

❑ Day Use $ _____
❑ Refund policy

_____

_____

_____

Notes:

Port Royal State Park
City: Clarksville   County: Montgomery

Plan your trip: https://tnstateparks.com/parks/radnor-lake

Activities:

- ❑ Biking
- ❑ Birding
- ❑ Boating
- ❑ Caving
- ❑ Disc Golf / Golf
- ❑ Fishing
- ❑ Hiking
- ❑ Hunting
- ❑ Paddling
- ❑ Rock Climbing
- ❑ Swimming
- ❑ Tours

- ❑ Watersports
- ❑ Wildlife Viewing
- ❑
- ❑
- ❑
- ❑
- ❑
- ❑
- ❑
- ❑
- ❑
- ❑

Facilities:

- ❑ ADA
- ❑ Gift Shop
- ❑ Museum
- ❑ Visitor Center
- ❑ Picnic sites
- ❑ Restrooms

- ❑
- ❑
- ❑
- ❑
- ❑
- ❑

Things to do in the area:

Get the Facts

- ❑ Phone 615-373-3467
- ❑ Park Hours

  _____

- ❑ Reservations? ____Y ____N

  date made_____

- ❑ Open all year? ____Y____N

  dates_____

- ❑ Dog friendly _____Y _____N

- ❑ Distance from home

  miles: _____

  hours: _____

- ❑ Address_____

  _____

  _____

Fees:

- ❑ Day Use $ _____
- ❑ Refund policy

  _____

  _____

  _____

Notes:

Notes:

Cumberland Plateau Region

Old Stone Fort State Archaeological Park

City: Manchester   County: Coffee

Plan your trip: https://tnstateparks.com/parks/old-stone-fort

Activities:

- ☐ Birding
- ☐ Biking
- ☐ Boating
- ☐ Caving
- ☐ Disc Golf / Golf
- ☐ Fishing
- ☐ Hiking
- ☐ Horseback Riding
- ☐ Hunting
- ☐ Interpretive Programs

- ☐ Mountain Biking
- ☐ Paddling
- ☐ Rock Climbing
- ☐ Swimming
- ☐ Waterfalls
- ☐ Water sports
- ☐ Wildlife Viewing
- ☐
- ☐
- ☐
- ☐

- ☐
- ☐
- ☐
- ☐
- ☐
- ☐
- ☐
- ☐
- ☐
- ☐
- ☐

Facilities:

- ☐ ADA
- ☐ Picnic sites
- ☐ Restrooms
- ☐ Showers
- ☐ Trailer Access
- ☐ Visitor center
- ☐ Group Camping
- ☐ RV Camp
- ☐ Rustic Camping
- ☐ Cabins / Yurts
- ☐ Day Use Area

Notes:

Get the Facts

- ☐ Phone   931-723-5073
- ☐ Park Hours

  _____

- ☐ Reservations? _____Y _____N

  date made_____

- ☐ Open all year _____Y_____N

  dates_____

- ☐ Check in time _____
- ☐ Check out time _____
- ☐ Pet friendly _____Y _____N
- ☐ Max RV length _____
- ☐ Distance from home

  miles: _____

  hours: _____

- ☐ Address_____

  _____

  _____

Fees:

- ☐ Day Use $ _____
- ☐ Camp Sites $ _____
- ☐ RV Sites $ _____
- ☐ Refund policy

  _____

  _____

  _____

Make It Personal

Trip dates: _____ | The weather was: Sunny Cloudy Rainy Stormy Snowy Foggy Warm Cold

Why I went:

_____

_____

How I got there: (circle all that apply) Plane Train Car Bus Bike Hike RV MC

_____

I went with:

_____

We stayed in (space, cabin # etc):

_____

Most relaxing day:

_____

_____

Something funny:

_____

_____

Someone we met:

_____

_____

Best story told:

_____

_____

The kids liked this:

_____

_____

The best food:

_____

_____

Games played:

_____

_____

Something disappointing:

_____

_____

Next time I'll do this differently:

_____

_____

Cumberland Mountain State Park
City: Crossville   County: Cumberland

Plan your trip: https://tnstateparks.com/parks/cumberland-mountain

Activities:

- ☐ Birding
- ☐ Biking
- ☐ Boating
- ☐ Caving
- ☐ Disc Golf / Golf
- ☐ Fishing
- ☐ Hiking
- ☐ Horseback Riding
- ☐ Hunting
- ☐ Interpretive Programs

- ☐ Mountain Biking
- ☐ Paddling
- ☐ Rock Climbing
- ☐ Swimming
- ☐ Waterfalls
- ☐ Water sports
- ☐ Wildlife Viewing
- ☐
- ☐
- ☐
- ☐

- ☐
- ☐
- ☐
- ☐
- ☐
- ☐
- ☐
- ☐
- ☐
- ☐
- ☐

Facilities:

- ☐ ADA
- ☐ Picnic sites
- ☐ Restrooms
- ☐ Showers
- ☐ Trailer Access
- ☐ Visitor center
- ☐ Group Camping
- ☐ RV Camp
- ☐ Rustic Camping
- ☐ Cabins / Yurts
- ☐ Day Use Area

Notes:

Get the Facts

- ☐ Phone   931-484-6138
- ☐ Park Hours

_____

- ☐ Reservations? ____Y ____N

date made_____

- ☐ Open all year ____Y____N

dates_____

- ☐ Check in time _____
- ☐ Check out time _____
- ☐ Pet friendly _____Y _____N
- ☐ Max RV length _____
- ☐ Distance from home

miles: _____

hours: _____

- ☐ Address_____

_____

_____

Fees:

- ☐ Day Use $ _____
- ☐ Camp Sites $ _____
- ☐ RV Sites $ _____
- ☐ Refund policy

_____

_____

_____

Make It Personal

Trip dates: _____ | The weather was: Sunny Cloudy Rainy Stormy Snowy Foggy Warm Cold

Why I went:
_____

_____

How I got there: (circle all that apply) Plane Train Car Bus Bike Hike RV MC

I went with:
_____

We stayed in (space, cabin # etc):
_____

Most relaxing day:
_____

_____

Something funny:
_____

_____

Someone we met:
_____

_____

Best story told:
_____

_____

The kids liked this:
_____

_____

The best food:
_____

_____

Games played:
_____

_____

Something disappointing:
_____

_____

Next time I'll do this differently:
_____

_____

Pickett CCC Memorial State Park

City: Jamestown   County: Fentress

Plan your trip: https://tnstateparks.com/parks/pickett

Activities:

- ❑ Birding
- ❑ Biking
- ❑ Boating
- ❑ Caving
- ❑ Disc Golf / Golf
- ❑ Fishing
- ❑ Hiking
- ❑ Horseback Riding
- ❑ Hunting
- ❑ Interpretive Programs

- ❑ Mountain Biking
- ❑ Paddling
- ❑ Rock Climbing
- ❑ Swimming
- ❑ Waterfalls
- ❑ Water sports
- ❑ Wildlife Viewing
- ❑
- ❑
- ❑
- ❑

- ❑
- ❑
- ❑
- ❑
- ❑
- ❑
- ❑
- ❑
- ❑
- ❑
- ❑

Facilities:

- ❑ ADA
- ❑ Picnic sites
- ❑ Restrooms
- ❑ Showers
- ❑ Trailer Access
- ❑ Visitor center
- ❑ Group Camping
- ❑ RV Camp
- ❑ Rustic Camping
- ❑ Cabins / Yurts
- ❑ Day Use Area

Notes:

Get the Facts

- ❑ Phone   931-879-5821
- ❑ Park Hours

    _____

- ❑ Reservations? _____Y _____N

    date made_____

- ❑ Open all year _____Y_____N

    dates_____

- ❑ Check in time _____
- ❑ Check out time _____
- ❑ Pet friendly _____Y _____N
- ❑ Max RV length _____
- ❑ Distance from home

    miles: _____

    hours: _____

- ❑ Address_____

    _____

    _____

Fees:

- ❑ Day Use $ _____
- ❑ Camp Sites $ _____
- ❑ RV Sites $ _____
- ❑ Refund policy

    _____

    _____

    _____

Make It Personal

Trip dates: _____   The weather was: Sunny Cloudy Rainy Stormy Snowy Foggy Warm Cold

Why I went: _____

_____

How I got there: (circle all that apply) Plane Train Car Bus Bike Hike RV MC

I went with: _____

We stayed in (space, cabin # etc): _____

Most relaxing day: _____

_____

Something funny: _____

_____

Someone we met: _____

_____

Best story told: _____

_____

The kids liked this: _____

_____

The best food: _____

_____

Games played: _____

_____

Something disappointing: _____

_____

Next time I'll do this differently: _____

_____

Tim's Ford State Park
City: Winchester   County: Franklin

Plan your trip: https://tnstateparks.com/parks/tims-ford

Activities:

- ❑ Birding
- ❑ Biking
- ❑ Boating
- ❑ Caving
- ❑ Disc Golf / Golf
- ❑ Fishing
- ❑ Hiking
- ❑ Horseback Riding
- ❑ Hunting
- ❑ Interpretive Programs

- ❑ Mountain Biking
- ❑ Paddling
- ❑ Rock Climbing
- ❑ Swimming
- ❑ Waterfalls
- ❑ Water sports
- ❑ Wildlife Viewing
- ❑
- ❑
- ❑
- ❑

- ❑
- ❑
- ❑
- ❑
- ❑
- ❑
- ❑
- ❑
- ❑
- ❑
- ❑

Facilities:

- ❑ ADA
- ❑ Picnic sites
- ❑ Restrooms
- ❑ Showers
- ❑ Trailer Access
- ❑ Visitor center
- ❑ Group Camping
- ❑ RV Camp
- ❑ Rustic Camping
- ❑ Cabins / Yurts
- ❑ Day Use Area

Notes:

Get the Facts

- ❑ Phone   931-968-3536
- ❑ Park Hours

  _____

- ❑ Reservations? ____Y ____N

  date made_____
- ❑ Open all year ____Y____N

  dates_____
- ❑ Check in time _____
- ❑ Check out time _____
- ❑ Pet friendly _____Y _____N
- ❑ Max RV length _____
- ❑ Distance from home

  miles: _____

  hours: _____
- ❑ Address_____

  _____

  _____

Fees:

- ❑ Day Use $ _____
- ❑ Camp Sites $ _____
- ❑ RV Sites $ _____
- ❑ Refund policy

  _____

  _____

  _____

Make It Personal

Trip dates: _____ | The weather was: Sunny Cloudy Rainy Stormy Snowy Foggy Warm Cold

Why I went:
_____

_____

How I got there: (circle all that apply) Plane Train Car Bus Bike Hike RV MC
_____

I went with:
_____

We stayed in (space, cabin # etc):
_____

Most relaxing day:
_____

_____

Something funny:
_____

_____

Someone we met:
_____

_____

Best story told:
_____

_____

The kids liked this:
_____

_____

The best food:
_____

_____

Games played:
_____

_____

Something disappointing:
_____

_____

Next time I'll do this differently:
_____

_____

South Cumberland State Park
City: Monteagle   County: Grundy
Plan your trip: https://tnstateparks.com/parks/south-cumberland

Activities:

- ❑ Birding
- ❑ Biking
- ❑ Boating
- ❑ Caving
- ❑ Disc Golf / Golf
- ❑ Fishing
- ❑ Hiking
- ❑ Horseback Riding
- ❑ Hunting
- ❑ Interpretive Programs

- ❑ Mountain Biking
- ❑ Paddling
- ❑ Rock Climbing
- ❑ Swimming
- ❑ Waterfalls
- ❑ Water sports
- ❑ Wildlife Viewing
- ❑
- ❑
- ❑
- ❑

- ❑
- ❑
- ❑
- ❑
- ❑
- ❑
- ❑
- ❑
- ❑
- ❑

Facilities:

- ❑ ADA
- ❑ Picnic sites
- ❑ Restrooms
- ❑ Showers
- ❑ Trailer Access
- ❑ Visitor center
- ❑ Group Camping
- ❑ RV Camp
- ❑ Rustic Camping
- ❑ Cabins / Yurts
- ❑ Day Use Area

Notes:

Get the Facts

- ❑ Phone   931-924-2980
- ❑ Park Hours

  _____

- ❑ Reservations? _____Y _____N

  date made_____

- ❑ Open all year _____Y_____N

  dates_____

- ❑ Check in time _____

- ❑ Check out time _____

- ❑ Pet friendly _____Y _____N

- ❑ Max RV length _____

- ❑ Distance from home

  miles: _____

  hours: _____

- ❑ Address_____

  _____

  _____

Fees:

- ❑ Day Use $ _____
- ❑ Camp Sites $ _____
- ❑ RV Sites $ _____
- ❑ Refund policy

  _____

  _____

  _____

Make It Personal

Trip dates: _____

The weather was: Sunny   Cloudy   Rainy   Stormy   Snowy   Foggy   Warm   Cold

Why I went: _____

_____

How I got there: (circle all that apply)   Plane   Train   Car   Bus   Bike   Hike   RV   MC

I went with: _____

We stayed in (space, cabin # etc): _____

Most relaxing day: _____

_____

Something funny: _____

_____

Someone we met: _____

_____

Best story told: _____

_____

The kids liked this: _____

_____

The best food: _____

_____

Games played: _____

_____

Something disappointing: _____

_____

Next time I'll do this differently: _____

_____

Bluff View Art District

City: Chattanooga   County: Hamilton

Plan your trip: https://bluffviewartdistrictchattanooga.com/

Activities:

- ❑ Birding
- ❑ Biking
- ❑ Boating
- ❑ Caving
- ❑ Disc Golf / Golf
- ❑ Fishing
- ❑ Hiking
- ❑ Horseback Riding
- ❑ Hunting
- ❑ Interpretive Programs

- ❑ Mountain Biking
- ❑ Paddling
- ❑ Rock Climbing
- ❑ Swimming
- ❑ Waterfalls
- ❑ Water sports
- ❑ Wildlife Viewing
- ❑
- ❑
- ❑
- ❑

- ❑
- ❑
- ❑
- ❑
- ❑
- ❑
- ❑
- ❑
- ❑
- ❑
- ❑

Facilities:

- ❑ ADA
- ❑ Picnic sites
- ❑ Restrooms
- ❑ Showers
- ❑ Trailer Access
- ❑ Visitor center
- ❑ Group Camping
- ❑ RV Camp
- ❑ Rustic Camping
- ❑ Cabins / Yurts
- ❑ Day Use Area

Notes:

Get the Facts

- ❑ Phone   423-321-0235
- ❑ Park Hours

  _____

- ❑ Reservations? ____Y ____N

  date made_____

- ❑ Open all year ____Y____N

  dates_____

- ❑ Check in time _____
- ❑ Check out time _____
- ❑ Pet friendly _____Y _____N
- ❑ Max RV length _____
- ❑ Distance from home

  miles: _____

  hours: _____

- ❑ Address_____

  _____

  _____

Fees:

- ❑ Day Use $ _____
- ❑ Camp Sites $ _____
- ❑ RV Sites $ _____
- ❑ Refund policy

  _____

  _____

  _____

Make It Personal

Trip dates: _____

The weather was: Sunny Cloudy Rainy Stormy Snowy Foggy Warm Cold

Why I went:
_____

_____

How I got there: (circle all that apply)   Plane   Train   Car   Bus   Bike   Hike   RV   MC

I went with:
_____

We stayed in (space, cabin # etc):
_____

Most relaxing day:
_____

_____

Something funny:
_____

_____

Someone we met:
_____

_____

Best story told:
_____

_____

The kids liked this:
_____

_____

The best food:
_____

_____

Games played:
_____

_____

Something disappointing:
_____

_____

Next time I'll do this differently:
_____

_____

Ruby Falls Cave & Waterfall
City: Chattanooga   County: Hamilton

Plan your trip: https://www.rubyfalls.com/

Activities:

- ❑ Birding
- ❑ Biking
- ❑ Boating
- ❑ Caving
- ❑ Disc Golf / Golf
- ❑ Fishing
- ❑ Hiking
- ❑ Horseback Riding
- ❑ Hunting
- ❑ Interpretive Programs

- ❑ Mountain Biking
- ❑ Paddling
- ❑ Rock Climbing
- ❑ Swimming
- ❑ Waterfalls
- ❑ Water sports
- ❑ Wildlife Viewing
- ❑
- ❑
- ❑
- ❑

- ❑
- ❑
- ❑
- ❑
- ❑
- ❑
- ❑
- ❑
- ❑
- ❑
- ❑

Facilities:

- ❑ ADA
- ❑ Picnic sites
- ❑ Restrooms
- ❑ Showers
- ❑ Trailer Access
- ❑ Visitor center
- ❑ Group Camping
- ❑ RV Camp
- ❑ Rustic Camping
- ❑ Cabins / Yurts
- ❑ Day Use Area

Notes:

Get the Facts

- ❑ Phone   423-821-2544
- ❑ Park Hours

_____

- ❑ Reservations? _____Y _____N

date made_____

- ❑ Open all year _____Y_____N

dates_____

- ❑ Check in time _____
- ❑ Check out time _____
- ❑ Pet friendly _____Y _____N
- ❑ Max RV length _____
- ❑ Distance from home

miles: _____

hours: _____

- ❑ Address_____

_____

_____

Fees:

- ❑ Day Use $ _____
- ❑ Camp Sites $ _____
- ❑ RV Sites $ _____
- ❑ Refund policy

_____

_____

_____

Make It Personal

Trip dates: _____

The weather was: Sunny Cloudy Rainy Stormy Snowy Foggy Warm Cold

Why I went: _____

_____

How I got there: (circle all that apply) Plane Train Car Bus Bike Hike RV MC

I went with: _____

We stayed in (space, cabin # etc): _____

Most relaxing day: _____

_____

Something funny: _____

_____

Someone we met: _____

_____

Best story told: _____

_____

The kids liked this: _____

_____

The best food: _____

_____

Games played: _____

_____

Something disappointing: _____

_____

Next time I'll do this differently: _____

_____

_____

Harrison Bay State Park
City: Harrison   County: Hamilton

Plan your trip: https://tnstateparks.com/parks/harrison-bay

Activities:

- ❑ Birding
- ❑ Biking
- ❑ Boating
- ❑ Caving
- ❑ Disc Golf / Golf
- ❑ Fishing
- ❑ Hiking
- ❑ Horseback Riding
- ❑ Hunting
- ❑ Interpretive Programs

- ❑ Mountain Biking
- ❑ Paddling
- ❑ Rock Climbing
- ❑ Swimming
- ❑ Waterfalls
- ❑ Water sports
- ❑ Wildlife Viewing
- ❑
- ❑
- ❑
- ❑

- ❑
- ❑
- ❑
- ❑
- ❑
- ❑
- ❑
- ❑
- ❑
- ❑
- ❑

Facilities:

- ❑ ADA
- ❑ Picnic sites
- ❑ Restrooms
- ❑ Showers
- ❑ Trailer Access
- ❑ Visitor center
- ❑ Group Camping
- ❑ RV Camp
- ❑ Rustic Camping
- ❑ Cabins / Yurts
- ❑ Day Use Area

Notes:

Get the Facts

- ❑ Phone   423-344-6214
- ❑ Park Hours

  _____

- ❑ Reservations? ____Y ____N

  date made_____
- ❑ Open all year ____Y____N

  dates_____
- ❑ Check in time _____
- ❑ Check out time _____
- ❑ Pet friendly _____Y _____N
- ❑ Max RV length _____
- ❑ Distance from home

  miles: _____

  hours: _____
- ❑ Address_____

  _____

  _____

Fees:

- ❑ Day Use $ _____
- ❑ Camp Sites $ _____
- ❑ RV Sites $ _____
- ❑ Refund policy

  _____

  _____

  _____

Make It Personal

Trip dates:

The weather was: Sunny Cloudy Rainy Stormy Snowy Foggy Warm Cold

Why I went:

How I got there: (circle all that apply) Plane Train Car Bus Bike Hike RV MC

I went with:

We stayed in (space, cabin # etc):

Most relaxing day:

Something funny:

Someone we met:

Best story told:

The kids liked this:

The best food:

Games played:

Something disappointing:

Next time I'll do this differently:

Standing Stone State Park
City: Hilham   County: Overton

Plan your trip: https://tnstateparks.com/parks/standing-stone

Activities:

- ❑ Birding
- ❑ Biking
- ❑ Boating
- ❑ Caving
- ❑ Disc Golf / Golf
- ❑ Fishing
- ❑ Hiking
- ❑ Horseback Riding
- ❑ Hunting
- ❑ Interpretive Programs

- ❑ Mountain Biking
- ❑ Paddling
- ❑ Rock Climbing
- ❑ Swimming
- ❑ Waterfalls
- ❑ Water sports
- ❑ Wildlife Viewing
- ❑
- ❑
- ❑
- ❑

- ❑
- ❑
- ❑
- ❑
- ❑
- ❑
- ❑
- ❑
- ❑
- ❑
- ❑

Facilities:

- ❑ ADA
- ❑ Picnic sites
- ❑ Restrooms
- ❑ Showers
- ❑ Trailer Access
- ❑ Visitor center
- ❑ Group Camping
- ❑ RV Camp
- ❑ Rustic Camping
- ❑ Cabins / Yurts
- ❑ Day Use Area

Notes:

Get the Facts

- ❑ Phone   931-823-6347
- ❑ Park Hours

  _____

- ❑ Reservations? _____Y _____N

  date made_____

- ❑ Open all year _____Y_____N

  dates_____

- ❑ Check in time _____

- ❑ Check out time _____

- ❑ Pet friendly _____Y _____N

- ❑ Max RV length _____

- ❑ Distance from home

  miles: _____

  hours: _____

- ❑ Address_____

  _____

  _____

Fees:

- ❑ Day Use $ _____
- ❑ Camp Sites $ _____
- ❑ RV Sites $ _____
- ❑ Refund policy

  _____

  _____

  _____

Make It Personal

Trip dates: _____ | The weather was: Sunny Cloudy Rainy Stormy Snowy Foggy Warm Cold

Why I went: _____

_____

How I got there: (circle all that apply)   Plane   Train   Car   Bus   Bike   Hike   RV   MC

I went with: _____

We stayed in (space, cabin # etc): _____

Most relaxing day: _____

_____

Something funny: _____

_____

Someone we met: _____

_____

Best story told: _____

_____

The kids liked this: _____

_____

The best food: _____

_____

Games played: _____

_____

Something disappointing: _____

_____

Next time I'll do this differently: _____

_____

Edgar Evins State Park
City: Silver Point   County: Putnam

Plan your trip: https://tnstateparks.com/parks/edgar-evins

Activities:

- ❑ Birding
- ❑ Biking
- ❑ Boating
- ❑ Caving
- ❑ Disc Golf / Golf
- ❑ Fishing
- ❑ Hiking
- ❑ Horseback Riding
- ❑ Hunting
- ❑ Interpretive Programs

- ❑ Mountain Biking
- ❑ Paddling
- ❑ Rock Climbing
- ❑ Swimming
- ❑ Waterfalls
- ❑ Water sports
- ❑ Wildlife Viewing
- ❑
- ❑
- ❑
- ❑

- ❑
- ❑
- ❑
- ❑
- ❑
- ❑
- ❑
- ❑
- ❑
- ❑
- ❑

Facilities:

- ❑ ADA
- ❑ Picnic sites
- ❑ Restrooms
- ❑ Showers
- ❑ Trailer Access
- ❑ Visitor center
- ❑ Group Camping
- ❑ RV Camp
- ❑ Rustic Camping
- ❑ Cabins / Yurts
- ❑ Day Use Area

Notes:

Get the Facts

- ❑ Phone   931-646-3080
- ❑ Park Hours

  _____

- ❑ Reservations? ____Y ____N

  date made_____

- ❑ Open all year ____Y____N

  dates_____

- ❑ Check in time _____

- ❑ Check out time _____

- ❑ Pet friendly _____Y _____N

- ❑ Max RV length _____

- ❑ Distance from home

  miles: _____

  hours: _____

- ❑ Address_____

  _____

  _____

Fees:

- ❑ Day Use $ _____
- ❑ Camp Sites $ _____
- ❑ RV Sites $ _____
- ❑ Refund policy

  _____

  _____

  _____

Make It Personal

Trip dates: _____ | The weather was: Sunny Cloudy Rainy Stormy Snowy Foggy Warm Cold

Why I went:
_____

_____

How I got there: (circle all that apply)   Plane   Train   Car   Bus   Bike   Hike   RV   MC
_____

I went with:
_____

We stayed in (space, cabin # etc):
_____

Most relaxing day:
_____

_____

Something funny:
_____

_____

Someone we met:
_____

_____

Best story told:
_____

_____

The kids liked this:
_____

_____

The best food:
_____

_____

Games played:
_____

_____

Something disappointing:
_____

_____

Next time I'll do this differently:
_____

_____

Fall Creek Falls State Park
City: Spencer   County: Van Buren

Plan your trip: https://tnstateparks.com/parks/fall-creek-falls

Activities:

- ❑ Birding
- ❑ Biking
- ❑ Boating
- ❑ Caving
- ❑ Disc Golf / Golf
- ❑ Fishing
- ❑ Hiking
- ❑ Horseback Riding
- ❑ Hunting
- ❑ Interpretive Programs

- ❑ Mountain Biking
- ❑ Paddling
- ❑ Rock Climbing
- ❑ Swimming
- ❑ Waterfalls
- ❑ Water sports
- ❑ Wildlife Viewing
- ❑
- ❑
- ❑
- ❑

- ❑
- ❑
- ❑
- ❑
- ❑
- ❑
- ❑
- ❑
- ❑
- ❑
- ❑

Facilities:

- ❑ ADA
- ❑ Picnic sites
- ❑ Restrooms
- ❑ Showers
- ❑ Trailer Access
- ❑ Visitor center
- ❑ Group Camping
- ❑ RV Camp
- ❑ Rustic Camping
- ❑ Cabins / Yurts
- ❑ Day Use Area

Notes:

Get the Facts

- ❑ Phone   423-881-5298
- ❑ Park Hours

  _____

- ❑ Reservations? _____Y _____N

  date made_____

- ❑ Open all year _____Y_____N

  dates_____

- ❑ Check in time _____

- ❑ Check out time _____

- ❑ Pet friendly _____Y _____N

- ❑ Max RV length _____

- ❑ Distance from home

  miles: _____

  hours: _____

- ❑ Address_____

  _____

  _____

Fees:

- ❑ Day Use $ _____
- ❑ Camp Sites $ _____
- ❑ RV Sites $ _____
- ❑ Refund policy

  _____

  _____

  _____

Make It Personal

Trip dates: | The weather was: Sunny   Cloudy   Rainy   Stormy   Snowy   Foggy   Warm   Cold

Why I went:

_____

_____

How I got there: (circle all that apply)   Plane   Train   Car   Bus   Bike   Hike   RV   MC

I went with:

_____

We stayed in (space, cabin # etc):

_____

Most relaxing day:

_____

_____

Something funny:

_____

_____

Someone we met:

_____

_____

Best story told:

_____

_____

The kids liked this:

_____

_____

The best food:

_____

_____

Games played:

_____

_____

Something disappointing:

_____

_____

Next time I'll do this differently:

_____

_____

Rock Island State Park
City: Rock Island   County: Warren

Plan your trip: https://tnstateparks.com/parks/rock-island

Activities:

- ❑ Birding
- ❑ Biking
- ❑ Boating
- ❑ Caving
- ❑ Disc Golf / Golf
- ❑ Fishing
- ❑ Hiking
- ❑ Horseback Riding
- ❑ Hunting
- ❑ Interpretive Programs

- ❑ Mountain Biking
- ❑ Paddling
- ❑ Rock Climbing
- ❑ Swimming
- ❑ Waterfalls
- ❑ Water sports
- ❑ Wildlife Viewing
- ❑
- ❑
- ❑
- ❑

- ❑
- ❑
- ❑
- ❑
- ❑
- ❑
- ❑
- ❑
- ❑
- ❑
- ❑

Facilities:

- ❑ ADA
- ❑ Picnic sites
- ❑ Restrooms
- ❑ Showers
- ❑ Trailer Access
- ❑ Visitor center
- ❑ Group Camping
- ❑ RV Camp
- ❑ Rustic Camping
- ❑ Cabins / Yurts
- ❑ Day Use Area

Notes:

Get the Facts

- ❑ Phone   931-837-4770
- ❑ Park Hours

  _____

- ❑ Reservations? ____Y ____N

  date made_____

- ❑ Open all year ____Y____N

  dates_____

- ❑ Check in time _____
- ❑ Check out time _____
- ❑ Pet friendly _____Y _____N
- ❑ Max RV length _____
- ❑ Distance from home

  miles: _____

  hours: _____

- ❑ Address_____

  _____

  _____

Fees:

- ❑ Day Use $ _____
- ❑ Camp Sites $ _____
- ❑ RV Sites $ _____
- ❑ Refund policy

  _____

  _____

  _____

Make It Personal

Trip dates: _____ | The weather was: Sunny   Cloudy   Rainy   Stormy   Snowy   Foggy   Warm   Cold

Why I went:

_____

_____

How I got there: (circle all that apply)   Plane   Train   Car   Bus   Bike   Hike   RV   MC

_____

I went with:

_____

We stayed in (space, cabin # etc):

_____

Most relaxing day:

_____

_____

Something funny:

_____

_____

Someone we met:

_____

_____

Best story told:

_____

_____

The kids liked this:

_____

_____

The best food:

_____

_____

Games played:

_____

_____

Something disappointing:

_____

_____

Next time I'll do this differently:

_____

_____

Moccasin Bend Archeological District
City: Chattanooga   County: Hamilton

Plan your trip: https://www.nps.gov/chch/learn/historyculture/moccasin-bend-national-archeological-district.htm

History:

Things To Do:

- ☐ ADA availability
- ☐ Public Restrooms
- ☐ Gift Shop
- ☐ Museum
- ☐ Visitor Center
- ☐ Picnic areas
- ☐ Chamber of Commerce
- ☐ Monuments
- ☐ Art Galleries
- ☐ Tours
- ☐ Street Art
- ☐ Natural Areas
- ☐ Living History
- ☐ Cemetery
- ☐ Amphitheater

Places I Want to Visit in the Area:

Restaurants:

Boutiques & Shops:

Monuments:

Museums:

Get the Facts

- ☐ Address_____

  _____

- ☐ Phone   706-866-9241
- ☐ Best season to visit

  _____

- ☐ Pet Friendly   Y   N
- ☐ Reservations?   Y   N

  date made_____

- ☐ Distance from home

  miles: _____

  hours: _____

Budget for this trip:

Parking	$
Food	$
Museums	$
Hotel	$
Shopping	$
Total	$

Notes:

Restaurant:

My Experience:

Shopping:

Best Find:

The shop I want to go back to:

Museum:

The coolest thing I learned about this area:

Other:

Rhea County Courthouse
City: Dayton   County: Rhea

Plan your trip: http://rheacountytn.com/relocation/departments/

History:

Get the Facts

- ❑ Address_____

  _____

- ❑ Phone   423-775-7801
- ❑ Best season to visit

  _____

- ❑ Pet Friendly   Y   N
- ❑ Reservations?   Y   N

  date made_____

- ❑ Distance from home

  miles: _____

  hours: _____

Things To Do:

- ❑ ADA availability
- ❑ Public Restrooms
- ❑ Gift Shop
- ❑ Museum
- ❑ Visitor Center
- ❑ Picnic areas
- ❑ Chamber of Commerce

- ❑ Monuments
- ❑ Art Galleries
- ❑ Tours
- ❑ Street Art
- ❑ Natural Areas
- ❑ Living History
- ❑ Cemetery
- ❑ Amphitheater

Places I Want to Visit in the Area:

Restaurants:

Boutiques & Shops:

Monuments:

Museums:

Budget for this trip:

Parking	$
Food	$
Museums	$
Hotel	$
Shopping	$
Total	$

Notes:

132

Restaurant:

My Experience:

Shopping:

Best Find:

The shop I want to go back to:

Museum:

The coolest thing I learned about this area:

Other:

Red Clay State Park
City: Cleveland   County: Bradley

Plan your trip: https://tnstateparks.com/parks/red-clay

Activities:

- ❏ Biking
- ❏ Birding
- ❏ Boating
- ❏ Caving
- ❏ Disc Golf / Golf
- ❏ Fishing
- ❏ Hiking
- ❏ Hunting
- ❏ Paddling
- ❏ Rock Climbing
- ❏ Swimming
- ❏ Tours

- ❏ Watersports
- ❏ Wildlife Viewing
- ❏
- ❏
- ❏
- ❏
- ❏
- ❏
- ❏
- ❏
- ❏
- ❏

Facilities:

- ❏ ADA
- ❏ Gift Shop
- ❏ Museum
- ❏ Visitor Center
- ❏ Picnic sites
- ❏ Restrooms

- ❏
- ❏
- ❏
- ❏
- ❏
- ❏

Things to do in the area:

Get the Facts

- ❏ Phone 423-478-0339
- ❏ Park Hours

  _____

- ❏ Reservations? ____Y ____N

  date made_____

- ❏ Open all year? ____Y____N

  dates_____

- ❏ Dog friendly _____Y _____N

- ❏ Distance from home

  miles: _____

  hours: _____

- ❏ Address_____

  _____

  _____

Fees:

- ❏ Day Use $ _____
- ❏ Refund policy

  _____
  _____
  _____

Notes:

Sgt. Alvin C. York State Historic Park
City: Pall Mall   County: Fentress

Plan your trip: https://tnstateparks.com/parks/sgt-alvin-c-york

Activities:

- ❑ Biking
- ❑ Birding
- ❑ Boating
- ❑ Caving
- ❑ Disc Golf / Golf
- ❑ Fishing
- ❑ Hiking
- ❑ Hunting
- ❑ Paddling
- ❑ Rock Climbing
- ❑ Swimming
- ❑ Tours

- ❑ Watersports
- ❑ Wildlife Viewing
- ❑
- ❑
- ❑
- ❑
- ❑
- ❑
- ❑
- ❑
- ❑
- ❑

Facilities:

- ❑ ADA
- ❑ Gift Shop
- ❑ Museum
- ❑ Visitor Center
- ❑ Picnic sites
- ❑ Restrooms

- ❑
- ❑
- ❑
- ❑
- ❑
- ❑

Things to do in the area:

Get the Facts

- ❑ Phone 931-879-6456
- ❑ Park Hours

_____

- ❑ Reservations? ____Y ____N

date made_____

- ❑ Open all year? ____Y____N

dates_____

- ❑ Dog friendly _____Y _____N
- ❑ Distance from home

miles: _____

hours: _____

- ❑ Address_____

_____

_____

Fees:

- ❑ Day Use $ _____
- ❑ Refund policy

_____

_____

_____

Notes:

Booker T. Washington State Park
City: Chattanooga   County: Hamilton

Plan your trip: https://tnstateparks.com/parks/booker-t-washington

Activities:

- ❑ Biking
- ❑ Birding
- ❑ Boating
- ❑ Caving
- ❑ Disc Golf / Golf
- ❑ Fishing
- ❑ Hiking
- ❑ Hunting
- ❑ Paddling
- ❑ Rock Climbing
- ❑ Swimming
- ❑ Tours

- ❑ Watersports
- ❑ Wildlife Viewing
- ❑
- ❑
- ❑
- ❑
- ❑
- ❑
- ❑
- ❑
- ❑
- ❑

Facilities:

- ❑ ADA
- ❑ Gift Shop
- ❑ Museum
- ❑ Visitor Center
- ❑ Picnic sites
- ❑ Restrooms

- ❑
- ❑
- ❑
- ❑
- ❑
- ❑

Things to do in the area:

Get the Facts

- ❑ Phone 423-894-4955
- ❑ Park Hours

_____

- ❑ Reservations? ____Y ____N

date made_____

- ❑ Open all year? ____Y____N

dates_____

- ❑ Dog friendly _____Y _____N
- ❑ Distance from home

miles: _____

hours: _____

- ❑ Address_____

_____

_____

Fees:

- ❑ Day Use $ _____
- ❑ Refund policy

_____

_____

_____

Notes:

136

Lookout Mountain
City: Chattanooga   County: Hamilton

Plan your trip: https://www.lookoutmountain.com/

Activities:

- ❑ Go Caving at Ruby Falls see page 116 for details
- ❑ Ride the Incline Railway, the world's steepest passenger railway

- ❑ Take a walk at Rock City Gardens and see the 100 ft waterfall

Facilities:

- ❑ ADA
- ❑ Gift Shop
- ❑ Museum
- ❑ Visitor Center
- ❑ Picnic sites
- ❑ Restrooms

- ❑ Restaurants
- ❑
- ❑
- ❑
- ❑
- ❑

Things to do in the area:

Get the Facts

- ❑ Phone 800-825-8366
- ❑ Park Hours

  _____

- ❑ Reservations? ____Y ____N

  date made_____

- ❑ Open all year? ____Y____N

  dates_____

- ❑ Dog friendly _____Y _____N
- ❑ Distance from home

  miles: _____

  hours: _____

- ❑ Address_____

  _____

  _____

Fees:

- ❑ Tour $ _____
- ❑ Tour $ _____
- ❑ Tour $_____
- ❑ Refund policy

  _____

Notes:

Cordell Hull Birthplace State Park
City: Byrdstown   County: Pickett

Plan your trip: https://tnstateparks.com/parks/cordell-hull-birthplace

Activities:

- ❑ Biking
- ❑ Birding
- ❑ Boating
- ❑ Caving
- ❑ Disc Golf / Golf
- ❑ Fishing
- ❑ Hiking
- ❑ Hunting
- ❑ Paddling
- ❑ Rock Climbing
- ❑ Swimming
- ❑ Tours
- ❑ Watersports
- ❑ Wildlife Viewing
- ❑
- ❑
- ❑
- ❑
- ❑
- ❑
- ❑
- ❑
- ❑
- ❑

Facilities:

- ❑ ADA
- ❑ Gift Shop
- ❑ Museum
- ❑ Visitor Center
- ❑ Picnic sites
- ❑ Restrooms
- ❑
- ❑
- ❑
- ❑
- ❑
- ❑

Things to do in the area:

Get the Facts

- ❑ Phone 931-864-3247
- ❑ Park Hours

_____

- ❑ Reservations? _____Y _____N

date made_____

- ❑ Open all year? _____Y_____N

dates_____

- ❑ Dog friendly _____Y _____N
- ❑ Distance from home

miles: _____

hours: _____

- ❑ Address_____

_____

_____

Fees:

- ❑ Day Use $ _____
- ❑ Refund policy

_____

_____

_____

Notes:

Cummins Falls State Park
City: Cookeville   County: Putnam

Plan your trip: https://tnstateparks.com/parks/cummins-falls

Activities:

- ❑ Biking
- ❑ Birding
- ❑ Boating
- ❑ Caving
- ❑ Disc Golf / Golf
- ❑ Fishing
- ❑ Hiking
- ❑ Hunting
- ❑ Paddling
- ❑ Rock Climbing
- ❑ Swimming
- ❑ Tours

- ❑ Watersports
- ❑ Wildlife Viewing
- ❑
- ❑
- ❑
- ❑
- ❑
- ❑
- ❑
- ❑
- ❑
- ❑

Facilities:

- ❑ ADA
- ❑ Gift Shop
- ❑ Museum
- ❑ Visitor Center
- ❑ Picnic sites
- ❑ Restrooms

- ❑
- ❑
- ❑
- ❑
- ❑
- ❑

Things to do in the area:

Get the Facts

- ❑ Phone 931-520-6691
- ❑ Park Hours

  _____

- ❑ Reservations? ____Y ____N

  date made_____

- ❑ Open all year? ____Y____N

  dates_____

- ❑ Dog friendly _____Y _____N
- ❑ Distance from home

  miles: _____

  hours: _____

- ❑ Address_____

  _____

  _____

Fees:

- ❑ Day Use $ _____
- ❑ Refund policy

  _____

  _____

  _____

Notes:

Burgess Falls State Park
City: Sparta   County: White

Plan your trip: https://tnstateparks.com/parks/burgess-falls

Activities:

- ❑ Biking
- ❑ Birding
- ❑ Boating
- ❑ Caving
- ❑ Disc Golf / Golf
- ❑ Fishing
- ❑ Hiking
- ❑ Hunting
- ❑ Paddling
- ❑ Rock Climbing
- ❑ Swimming
- ❑ Tours

- ❑ Watersports
- ❑ Wildlife Viewing
- ❑
- ❑
- ❑
- ❑
- ❑
- ❑
- ❑
- ❑
- ❑
- ❑

Facilities:

- ❑ ADA
- ❑ Gift Shop
- ❑ Museum
- ❑ Visitor Center
- ❑ Picnic sites
- ❑ Restrooms

- ❑
- ❑
- ❑
- ❑
- ❑
- ❑

Things to do in the area:

Get the Facts

- ❑ Phone 931-432-5312
- ❑ Park Hours

_____

- ❑ Reservations? ____Y ____N

date made_____

- ❑ Open all year? ____Y____N

dates_____

- ❑ Dog friendly _____Y _____N
- ❑ Distance from home

miles: _____

hours: _____

- ❑ Address_____

_____

_____

Fees:

- ❑ Day Use $ _____
- ❑ Refund policy

_____

_____

_____

Notes:

Window Cliffs State Natural Area
City: Sparta   County: White

Plan your trip: https://www.tn.gov/environment/program-areas/na-natural-areas/natural-areas-middle-region/middle-region/na-na-window-cliffs.html

Activities:

- ❑ Biking
- ❑ Birding
- ❑ Boating
- ❑ Caving
- ❑ Disc Golf / Golf
- ❑ Fishing
- ❑ Hiking
- ❑ Hunting
- ❑ Paddling
- ❑ Rock Climbing
- ❑ Swimming
- ❑ Tours

- ❑ Watersports
- ❑ Wildlife Viewing
- ❑
- ❑
- ❑
- ❑
- ❑
- ❑
- ❑
- ❑
- ❑
- ❑

Facilities:

- ❑ ADA
- ❑ Gift Shop
- ❑ Museum
- ❑ Visitor Center
- ❑ Picnic sites
- ❑ Restrooms

- ❑
- ❑
- ❑
- ❑
- ❑
- ❑

Things to do in the area:

Get the Facts

- ❑ Phone 931-432-5312
- ❑ Park Hours

    _____

- ❑ Reservations? ____Y ____N

    date made_____

- ❑ Open all year? ____Y____N

    dates_____

- ❑ Dog friendly _____Y _____N
- ❑ Distance from home

    miles: _____

    hours: _____

- ❑ Address_____

    _____

    _____

Fees:

- ❑ Day Use $ _____
- ❑ Refund policy

    _____

    _____

    _____

Notes:

Tennessee Trivia

1. What location is considered by many to be the birthplace of the blues?
A. Beale Street Historic District
B. Cooper-Young Historic District
C. Collierville Historic District
D. None of the above

2. Which artists got their start at Sun Records?
A. Elvis Presley & Johnny Cash
B. Carl Perkins & Jerry Lee Lewis
C. Roy Orbison & Charlie Rich
D. All of the above

3. Where is there a memorial of John Lewis' reputable sit-in at segregated lunch counters memorialized?
A. Radnor Lake State Natural Area & Music Row
B. Jubilee Hall at Fisk University & Bluff View Art District
C. Bicentennial Capitol Mall State Park & Nashville Downtown Library
D. None of the above

4. What are the names of the three brick-and-mortar museums that recognize Tennessee's Role in nurturing popular music?
A. The Memphis Rock N' Roll Soul
B. Country Music Hall of Fame
C. International Rock-A-Billy
D. All of the above

5. How many US Presidents were born in Tennessee?
A. 3
B. 0
C. 2

6. Which famous TN frontiersman was killed at the Alamo?
A. David Crockett
B. James K. Polk
C. Sequoyah

7. Where was the civil war battle called "The Battle Above the Clouds" fought?
A. Lookout Mountain
B. James White's Fort
C. Swaggerty Fort Historic Site

8. In what city is Elvis Presley's Graceland residence and tomb?
A. Nashville
B. Memphis
C. Knoxville

9. The first settlement in middle TN located in Castalian Springs is called what?
A. Hawthorne Hill
B. Bledsoe Creek State Park
C. Wynnewood State Historic Site

10. Which national park located in TN is the most visited in the nation?
A. Chickamauga & Chattanooga National Military Park
B. Great Smoky Mountains National Park
C. Appalachian National Scenic Trail

East Region

Cove Lake State Park
City: Caryville   County: Campbell

Plan your trip: https://tnstateparks.com/parks/cove-lake

Activities:

- ❑ Birding
- ❑ Biking
- ❑ Boating
- ❑ Caving
- ❑ Disc Golf / Golf
- ❑ Fishing
- ❑ Hiking
- ❑ Horseback Riding
- ❑ Hunting
- ❑ Interpretive Programs
- ❑ Mountain Biking
- ❑ Paddling
- ❑ Rock Climbing
- ❑ Swimming
- ❑ Waterfalls
- ❑ Water sports
- ❑ Wildlife Viewing
- ❑
- ❑
- ❑
- ❑
- ❑
- ❑
- ❑
- ❑
- ❑
- ❑
- ❑
- ❑
- ❑
- ❑

Facilities:

- ❑ ADA
- ❑ Picnic sites
- ❑ Restrooms
- ❑ Showers
- ❑ Trailer Access
- ❑ Visitor center
- ❑ Group Camping
- ❑ RV Camp
- ❑ Rustic Camping
- ❑ Cabins / Yurts
- ❑ Day Use Area

Notes:

Get the Facts

- ❑ Phone   423-566-9701
- ❑ Park Hours

  _____

- ❑ Reservations? _____Y _____N

  date made_____

- ❑ Open all year _____Y_____N

  dates_____

- ❑ Check in time _____
- ❑ Check out time _____
- ❑ Pet friendly _____Y _____N
- ❑ Max RV length _____
- ❑ Distance from home

  miles: _____

  hours: _____

- ❑ Address_____

  _____

  _____

Fees:

- ❑ Day Use $ _____
- ❑ Camp Sites $ _____
- ❑ RV Sites $ _____
- ❑ Refund policy

  _____

  _____

  _____

Make It Personal

Trip dates: _____ | The weather was: Sunny Cloudy Rainy Stormy Snowy Foggy Warm Cold

Why I went:

_____

_____

How I got there: (circle all that apply)   Plane   Train   Car   Bus   Bike   Hike   RV   MC

_____

I went with:

_____

We stayed in (space, cabin # etc):

_____

Most relaxing day:

_____

_____

Something funny:

_____

_____

Someone we met:

_____

_____

Best story told:

_____

_____

The kids liked this:

_____

_____

The best food:

_____

_____

Games played:

_____

_____

Something disappointing:

_____

_____

Next time I'll do this differently:

_____

_____

Justin P. Wilson Cumberland Trail State Park

City: Caryville   County: Campbell

Plan your trip: https://tnstateparks.com/parks/cumberland-trail

Activities:

- ☐ Birding
- ☐ Biking
- ☐ Boating
- ☐ Caving
- ☐ Disc Golf / Golf
- ☐ Fishing
- ☐ Hiking
- ☐ Horseback Riding
- ☐ Hunting
- ☐ Interpretive Programs
- ☐ Mountain Biking
- ☐ Paddling
- ☐ Rock Climbing
- ☐ Swimming
- ☐ Waterfalls
- ☐ Water sports
- ☐ Wildlife Viewing
- ☐
- ☐
- ☐
- ☐
- ☐
- ☐
- ☐
- ☐
- ☐
- ☐
- ☐
- ☐

Facilities:

- ☐ ADA
- ☐ Picnic sites
- ☐ Restrooms
- ☐ Showers
- ☐ Trailer Access
- ☐ Visitor center
- ☐ Group Camping
- ☐ RV Camp
- ☐ Rustic Camping
- ☐ Cabins / Yurts
- ☐ Day Use Area

Notes:

Get the Facts

- ☐ Phone   423-566-2229
- ☐ Park Hours

  _____

- ☐ Reservations? _____Y _____N

  date made_____

- ☐ Open all year _____Y_____N

  dates_____

- ☐ Check in time _____
- ☐ Check out time _____
- ☐ Pet friendly _____Y _____N
- ☐ Max RV length _____
- ☐ Distance from home

  miles: _____

  hours: _____

- ☐ Address_____

  _____

  _____

Fees:

- ☐ Day Use $ _____
- ☐ Camp Sites $ _____
- ☐ RV Sites $ _____
- ☐ Refund policy

  _____

  _____

  _____

Make It Personal

Trip dates:

The weather was: Sunny Cloudy Rainy Stormy Snowy Foggy Warm Cold

Why I went:

How I got there: (circle all that apply) Plane Train Car Bus Bike Hike RV MC

I went with:

We stayed in (space, cabin # etc):

Most relaxing day:

Something funny:

Someone we met:

Best story told:

The kids liked this:

The best food:

Games played:

Something disappointing:

Next time I'll do this differently:

Indian Mountain State Park
City: Jellico   County: Campbell

Plan your trip: https://tnstateparks.com/parks/indian-mountain

Activities:

- ❑ Birding
- ❑ Biking
- ❑ Boating
- ❑ Caving
- ❑ Disc Golf / Golf
- ❑ Fishing
- ❑ Hiking
- ❑ Horseback Riding
- ❑ Hunting
- ❑ Interpretive Programs

- ❑ Mountain Biking
- ❑ Paddling
- ❑ Rock Climbing
- ❑ Swimming
- ❑ Waterfalls
- ❑ Water sports
- ❑ Wildlife Viewing
- ❑
- ❑
- ❑
- ❑

- ❑
- ❑
- ❑
- ❑
- ❑
- ❑
- ❑
- ❑
- ❑
- ❑
- ❑

Facilities:

- ❑ ADA
- ❑ Picnic sites
- ❑ Restrooms
- ❑ Showers
- ❑ Trailer Access
- ❑ Visitor center
- ❑ Group Camping
- ❑ RV Camp
- ❑ Rustic Camping
- ❑ Cabins / Yurts
- ❑ Day Use Area

Notes:

Get the Facts

- ❑ Phone   423-566-5870
- ❑ Park Hours

    _____

- ❑ Reservations? ____Y ____N

    date made_____

- ❑ Open all year ____Y_____N

    dates_____

- ❑ Check in time _____
- ❑ Check out time _____
- ❑ Pet friendly _____Y _____N
- ❑ Max RV length _____
- ❑ Distance from home

    miles: _____

    hours: _____

- ❑ Address_____

    _____

    _____

Fees:

- ❑ Day Use $ _____
- ❑ Camp Sites $ _____
- ❑ RV Sites $ _____
- ❑ Refund policy

    _____

    _____

    _____

Make It Personal

Trip dates:

The weather was: Sunny Cloudy Rainy Stormy Snowy Foggy Warm Cold

Why I went:

_____

_____

How I got there: (circle all that apply)   Plane   Train   Car   Bus   Bike   Hike   RV   MC

_____

I went with:

_____

We stayed in (space, cabin # etc):

_____

Most relaxing day:

_____

_____

Something funny:

_____

_____

Someone we met:

_____

_____

Best story told:

_____

_____

The kids liked this:

_____

_____

The best food:

_____

_____

Games played:

_____

_____

Something disappointing:

_____

_____

Next time I'll do this differently:

_____

_____

Norris Dam State Park
City: Rocky Top   County: Campbell

Plan your trip: https://tnstateparks.com/parks/norris-dam

Activities:

- ❏ Birding
- ❏ Biking
- ❏ Boating
- ❏ Caving
- ❏ Disc Golf / Golf
- ❏ Fishing
- ❏ Hiking
- ❏ Horseback Riding
- ❏ Hunting
- ❏ Interpretive Programs
- ❏ Mountain Biking
- ❏ Paddling
- ❏ Rock Climbing
- ❏ Swimming
- ❏ Waterfalls
- ❏ Water sports
- ❏ Wildlife Viewing
- ❏
- ❏
- ❏
- ❏
- ❏
- ❏
- ❏
- ❏
- ❏
- ❏
- ❏
- ❏

Facilities:

- ❏ ADA
- ❏ Picnic sites
- ❏ Restrooms
- ❏ Showers
- ❏ Trailer Access
- ❏ Visitor center
- ❏ Group Camping
- ❏ RV Camp
- ❏ Rustic Camping
- ❏ Cabins / Yurts
- ❏ Day Use Area

Notes:

Get the Facts

- ❏ Phone   865-425-4500
- ❏ Park Hours

  _____

- ❏ Reservations? _____Y _____N

  date made_____

- ❏ Open all year _____Y_____N

  dates_____

- ❏ Check in time _____
- ❏ Check out time _____
- ❏ Pet friendly _____Y _____N
- ❏ Max RV length _____
- ❏ Distance from home

  miles: _____

  hours: _____

- ❏ Address_____

  _____

  _____

Fees:

- ❏ Day Use $ _____
- ❏ Camp Sites $ _____
- ❏ RV Sites $ _____
- ❏ Refund policy

  _____

  _____

  _____

Make It Personal

Trip dates: | The weather was: Sunny Cloudy Rainy Stormy Snowy Foggy Warm Cold

Why I went:

_____

_____

How I got there: (circle all that apply) Plane Train Car Bus Bike Hike RV MC

I went with:

_____

We stayed in (space, cabin # etc):

_____

Most relaxing day:

_____

Something funny:

_____

Someone we met:

_____

Best story told:

_____

The kids liked this:

_____

The best food:

_____

Games played:

_____

Something disappointing:

_____

Next time I'll do this differently:

_____

_____

Roan Mountain State Park
City: Roan Mountain   County: Carter

Plan your trip: https://tnstateparks.com/parks/roan-mountain

Activities:

- ❑ Birding
- ❑ Biking
- ❑ Boating
- ❑ Caving
- ❑ Disc Golf / Golf
- ❑ Fishing
- ❑ Hiking
- ❑ Horseback Riding
- ❑ Hunting
- ❑ Interpretive Programs

- ❑ Mountain Biking
- ❑ Paddling
- ❑ Rock Climbing
- ❑ Swimming
- ❑ Waterfalls
- ❑ Water sports
- ❑ Wildlife Viewing
- ❑
- ❑
- ❑
- ❑

- ❑
- ❑
- ❑
- ❑
- ❑
- ❑
- ❑
- ❑
- ❑
- ❑
- ❑

Facilities:

- ❑ ADA
- ❑ Picnic sites
- ❑ Restrooms
- ❑ Showers
- ❑ Trailer Access
- ❑ Visitor center
- ❑ Group Camping
- ❑ RV Camp
- ❑ Rustic Camping
- ❑ Cabins / Yurts
- ❑ Day Use Area

Notes:

Get the Facts

- ❑ Phone   423-547-3900
- ❑ Park Hours

  _____

- ❑ Reservations? ____Y ____N

  date made_____
- ❑ Open all year ____Y____N

  dates_____
- ❑ Check in time _____
- ❑ Check out time _____
- ❑ Pet friendly _____Y _____N
- ❑ Max RV length _____
- ❑ Distance from home

  miles: _____

  hours: _____
- ❑ Address_____

  _____

  _____

Fees:

- ❑ Day Use $ _____
- ❑ Camp Sites $ _____
- ❑ RV Sites $ _____
- ❑ Refund policy

  _____

  _____

  _____

Make It Personal

Trip dates:

The weather was: Sunny Cloudy Rainy Stormy Snowy Foggy Warm Cold

Why I went:

How I got there: (circle all that apply)   Plane   Train   Car   Bus   Bike   Hike   RV   MC

I went with:

We stayed in (space, cabin # etc):

Most relaxing day:

Something funny:

Someone we met:

Best story told:

The kids liked this:

The best food:

Games played:

Something disappointing:

Next time I'll do this differently:

Panther Creek State Park
City: Morristown   County: Hamblen

Plan your trip: https://tnstateparks.com/parks/panther-creek

Activities:

- ❑ Birding
- ❑ Biking
- ❑ Boating
- ❑ Caving
- ❑ Disc Golf / Golf
- ❑ Fishing
- ❑ Hiking
- ❑ Horseback Riding
- ❑ Hunting
- ❑ Interpretive Programs
- ❑ Mountain Biking
- ❑ Paddling
- ❑ Rock Climbing
- ❑ Swimming
- ❑ Waterfalls
- ❑ Water sports
- ❑ Wildlife Viewing
- ❑
- ❑
- ❑
- ❑
- ❑
- ❑
- ❑
- ❑
- ❑
- ❑
- ❑
- ❑
- ❑

Facilities:

- ❑ ADA
- ❑ Picnic sites
- ❑ Restrooms
- ❑ Showers
- ❑ Trailer Access
- ❑ Visitor center
- ❑ Group Camping
- ❑ RV Camp
- ❑ Rustic Camping
- ❑ Cabins / Yurts
- ❑ Day Use Area

Notes:

Get the Facts

- ❑ Phone   423-587-7046
- ❑ Park Hours

  _____

- ❑ Reservations? _____Y _____N

  date made_____
- ❑ Open all year _____Y_____N

  dates_____
- ❑ Check in time _____
- ❑ Check out time _____
- ❑ Pet friendly _____Y _____N
- ❑ Max RV length _____
- ❑ Distance from home

  miles: _____

  hours: _____
- ❑ Address_____

  _____

  _____

Fees:

- ❑ Day Use $ _____
- ❑ Camp Sites $ _____
- ❑ RV Sites $ _____
- ❑ Refund policy

  _____

  _____

  _____

Make It Personal

Trip dates: _____ | The weather was: Sunny Cloudy Rainy Stormy Snowy Foggy Warm Cold

Why I went: _____

_____

How I got there: (circle all that apply)   Plane   Train   Car   Bus   Bike   Hike   RV   MC
_____

I went with: _____

We stayed in (space, cabin # etc): _____

Most relaxing day: _____

_____

Something funny: _____

_____

Someone we met: _____

_____

Best story told: _____

_____

The kids liked this: _____

_____

The best food: _____

_____

Games played: _____

_____

Something disappointing: _____

_____

Next time I'll do this differently: _____

_____

Frozen Head State Park
City: Wartburg   County: Morgan
Plan your trip: https://tnstateparks.com/parks/frozen-head

Activities:

- ❑ Birding
- ❑ Biking
- ❑ Boating
- ❑ Caving
- ❑ Disc Golf / Golf
- ❑ Fishing
- ❑ Hiking
- ❑ Horseback Riding
- ❑ Hunting
- ❑ Interpretive Programs

- ❑ Mountain Biking
- ❑ Paddling
- ❑ Rock Climbing
- ❑ Swimming
- ❑ Waterfalls
- ❑ Water sports
- ❑ Wildlife Viewing
- ❑
- ❑
- ❑
- ❑

- ❑
- ❑
- ❑
- ❑
- ❑
- ❑
- ❑
- ❑
- ❑
- ❑
- ❑

Facilities:

- ❑ ADA
- ❑ Picnic sites
- ❑ Restrooms
- ❑ Showers
- ❑ Trailer Access
- ❑ Visitor center
- ❑ Group Camping
- ❑ RV Camp
- ❑ Rustic Camping
- ❑ Cabins / Yurts
- ❑ Day Use Area

Notes:

Get the Facts

- ❑ Phone   423-346-3318
- ❑ Park Hours

_____

- ❑ Reservations? ـــــــ Y ـــــــ N

date made_____

- ❑ Open all year ـــــــ Y ـــــــ N

dates_____

- ❑ Check in time _____
- ❑ Check out time _____
- ❑ Pet friendly _____ Y _____ N
- ❑ Max RV length _____
- ❑ Distance from home

miles: _____

hours: _____

- ❑ Address_____

_____

_____

Fees:

- ❑ Day Use $ _____
- ❑ Camp Sites $ _____
- ❑ RV Sites $ _____
- ❑ Refund policy

_____

_____

_____

Make It Personal

Trip dates: _____ | The weather was: Sunny Cloudy Rainy Stormy Snowy Foggy Warm Cold

Why I went: _____

_____

How I got there: (circle all that apply)   Plane   Train   Car   Bus   Bike   Hike   RV   MC

I went with: _____

We stayed in (space, cabin # etc): _____

Most relaxing day: _____

_____

Something funny: _____

_____

Someone we met: _____

_____

Best story told: _____

_____

The kids liked this: _____

_____

The best food: _____

_____

Games played: _____

_____

Something disappointing: _____

_____

Next time I'll do this differently: _____

_____

_____

Hiwassee/Ocoee Scenic River State Park

City: Delano   County: Polk

Plan your trip: https://tnstateparks.com/parks/hiwassee-ocoee

Activities:

- ❑ Birding
- ❑ Biking
- ❑ Boating
- ❑ Caving
- ❑ Disc Golf / Golf
- ❑ Fishing
- ❑ Hiking
- ❑ Horseback Riding
- ❑ Hunting
- ❑ Interpretive Programs

- ❑ Mountain Biking
- ❑ Paddling
- ❑ Rock Climbing
- ❑ Swimming
- ❑ Waterfalls
- ❑ Water sports
- ❑ Wildlife Viewing
- ❑
- ❑
- ❑
- ❑

- ❑
- ❑
- ❑
- ❑
- ❑
- ❑
- ❑
- ❑
- ❑
- ❑
- ❑

Facilities:

- ❑ ADA
- ❑ Picnic sites
- ❑ Restrooms
- ❑ Showers
- ❑ Trailer Access
- ❑ Visitor center
- ❑ Group Camping
- ❑ RV Camp
- ❑ Rustic Camping
- ❑ Cabins / Yurts
- ❑ Day Use Area

Notes:

Get the Facts

- ❑ Phone   423-263-0050
- ❑ Park Hours

  _____

- ❑ Reservations? ____Y ____N

  date made_____

- ❑ Open all year ____Y ____N

  dates_____

- ❑ Check in time _____
- ❑ Check out time _____
- ❑ Pet friendly _____Y _____N
- ❑ Max RV length _____
- ❑ Distance from home

  miles: _____

  hours: _____

- ❑ Address_____

  _____

  _____

Fees:

- ❑ Day Use $ _____
- ❑ Camp Sites $ _____
- ❑ RV Sites $ _____
- ❑ Refund policy

  _____

  _____

  _____

Make It Personal

Trip dates: _____ | The weather was: Sunny Cloudy Rainy Stormy Snowy Foggy Warm Cold

Why I went:
_____
_____

How I got there: (circle all that apply)   Plane   Train   Car   Bus   Bike   Hike   RV   MC
_____

I went with:
_____

We stayed in (space, cabin # etc):
_____

Most relaxing day:
_____
_____

Something funny:
_____
_____

Someone we met:
_____
_____

Best story told:
_____
_____

The kids liked this:
_____
_____

The best food:
_____
_____

Games played:
_____
_____

Something disappointing:
_____
_____

Next time I'll do this differently:
_____
_____

Noah Bud Ogle Cabin
City: Gatlinburg   County: Sevier

Plan your trip: http://www.hikinginthesmokys.com/ogle-place.htm

Activities:

- ☐ Birding
- ☐ Biking
- ☐ Boating
- ☐ Caving
- ☐ Disc Golf / Golf
- ☐ Fishing
- ☐ Hiking
- ☐ Horseback Riding
- ☐ Hunting
- ☐ Interpretive Programs

- ☐ Mountain Biking
- ☐ Paddling
- ☐ Rock Climbing
- ☐ Swimming
- ☐ Waterfalls
- ☐ Water sports
- ☐ Wildlife Viewing
- ☐
- ☐
- ☐
- ☐

- ☐
- ☐
- ☐
- ☐
- ☐
- ☐
- ☐
- ☐
- ☐
- ☐
- ☐

Facilities:

- ☐ ADA
- ☐ Picnic sites
- ☐ Restrooms
- ☐ Showers
- ☐ Trailer Access
- ☐ Visitor center
- ☐ Group Camping
- ☐ RV Camp
- ☐ Rustic Camping
- ☐ Cabins / Yurts
- ☐ Day Use Area

Notes:

Get the Facts

- ☐ Phone   865-436-4990
- ☐ Park Hours

_____

- ☐ Reservations? ____Y ____N

date made_____

- ☐ Open all year ____Y____N

dates_____

- ☐ Check in time _____
- ☐ Check out time _____
- ☐ Pet friendly _____Y _____N
- ☐ Max RV length _____
- ☐ Distance from home

miles: _____

hours: _____

- ☐ Address_____

_____

_____

Fees:

- ☐ Day Use $ _____
- ☐ Camp Sites $ _____
- ☐ RV Sites $ _____
- ☐ Refund policy

_____

_____

_____

Make It Personal

Trip dates: _____ | The weather was: Sunny Cloudy Rainy Stormy Snowy Foggy Warm Cold

Why I went:
_____

_____

How I got there: (circle all that apply)   Plane   Train   Car   Bus   Bike   Hike   RV   MC
_____

I went with:
_____

We stayed in (space, cabin # etc):
_____

Most relaxing day:
_____

_____

Something funny:
_____

_____

Someone we met:
_____

_____

Best story told:
_____

_____

The kids liked this:
_____

_____

The best food:
_____

_____

Games played:
_____

_____

Something disappointing:
_____

_____

Next time I'll do this differently:
_____

_____

Warriors' Path State Park
City: Kingsport   County: Sullivan

Plan your trip: https://tnstateparks.com/parks/warriors-path

Activities:

- ❑ Birding
- ❑ Biking
- ❑ Boating
- ❑ Caving
- ❑ Disc Golf / Golf
- ❑ Fishing
- ❑ Hiking
- ❑ Horseback Riding
- ❑ Hunting
- ❑ Interpretive Programs
- ❑ Mountain Biking
- ❑ Paddling
- ❑ Rock Climbing
- ❑ Swimming
- ❑ Waterfalls
- ❑ Water sports
- ❑ Wildlife Viewing
- ❑
- ❑
- ❑
- ❑
- ❑
- ❑
- ❑
- ❑
- ❑
- ❑
- ❑
- ❑
- ❑
- ❑

Facilities:

- ❑ ADA
- ❑ Picnic sites
- ❑ Restrooms
- ❑ Showers
- ❑ Trailer Access
- ❑ Visitor center
- ❑ Group Camping
- ❑ RV Camp
- ❑ Rustic Camping
- ❑ Cabins / Yurts
- ❑ Day Use Area

Notes:

Get the Facts

- ❑ Phone   423-239-8531
- ❑ Park Hours

  _____

- ❑ Reservations? ____Y ____N

  date made_____

- ❑ Open all year ____Y_____N

  dates_____

- ❑ Check in time _____
- ❑ Check out time _____
- ❑ Pet friendly _____Y _____N
- ❑ Max RV length _____
- ❑ Distance from home

  miles: _____

  hours: _____

- ❑ Address_____

  _____

  _____

Fees:

- ❑ Day Use $ _____
- ❑ Camp Sites $ _____
- ❑ RV Sites $ _____
- ❑ Refund policy

  _____

  _____

  _____

Make It Personal

Trip dates:

The weather was: Sunny Cloudy Rainy Stormy Snowy Foggy Warm Cold

Why I went:

How I got there: (circle all that apply) Plane Train Car Bus Bike Hike RV MC

I went with:

We stayed in (space, cabin # etc):

Most relaxing day:

Something funny:

Someone we met:

Best story told:

The kids liked this:

The best food:

Games played:

Something disappointing:

Next time I'll do this differently:

Big Ridge State Park
City: Maynardville   County: Union

Plan your trip: https://tnstateparks.com/parks/big-ridge

Activities:

- ❏ Birding
- ❏ Biking
- ❏ Boating
- ❏ Caving
- ❏ Disc Golf / Golf
- ❏ Fishing
- ❏ Hiking
- ❏ Horseback Riding
- ❏ Hunting
- ❏ Interpretive Programs

- ❏ Mountain Biking
- ❏ Paddling
- ❏ Rock Climbing
- ❏ Swimming
- ❏ Waterfalls
- ❏ Water sports
- ❏ Wildlife Viewing
- ❏
- ❏
- ❏
- ❏

- ❏
- ❏
- ❏
- ❏
- ❏
- ❏
- ❏
- ❏
- ❏
- ❏
- ❏

Facilities:

- ❏ ADA
- ❏ Picnic sites
- ❏ Restrooms
- ❏ Showers
- ❏ Trailer Access
- ❏ Visitor center
- ❏ Group Camping
- ❏ RV Camp
- ❏ Rustic Camping
- ❏ Cabins / Yurts
- ❏ Day Use Area

Notes:

Get the Facts

- ❏ Phone   865-992-5523
- ❏ Park Hours

  _____

- ❏ Reservations? ____Y ____N

  date made_____

- ❏ Open all year ____Y____N

  dates_____

- ❏ Check in time _____
- ❏ Check out time _____
- ❏ Pet friendly _____Y _____N
- ❏ Max RV length _____
- ❏ Distance from home

  miles: _____

  hours: _____

- ❏ Address_____

  _____

  _____

Fees:

- ❏ Day Use $ _____
- ❏ Camp Sites $ _____
- ❏ RV Sites $ _____
- ❏ Refund policy

  _____

  _____

  _____

Make It Personal

Trip dates:

The weather was: Sunny Cloudy Rainy Stormy Snowy Foggy Warm Cold

Why I went:

How I got there: (circle all that apply) Plane Train Car Bus Bike Hike RV MC

I went with:

We stayed in (space, cabin # etc):

Most relaxing day:

Something funny:

Someone we met:

Best story told:

The kids liked this:

The best food:

Games played:

Something disappointing:

Next time I'll do this differently:

David Crockett Birthplace State Park
City: Limestone   County: Washington

Plan your trip: https://tnstateparks.com/parks/david-crockett-birthplace

Activities:

- ❑ Birding
- ❑ Biking
- ❑ Boating
- ❑ Caving
- ❑ Disc Golf / Golf
- ❑ Fishing
- ❑ Hiking
- ❑ Horseback Riding
- ❑ Hunting
- ❑ Interpretive Programs

- ❑ Mountain Biking
- ❑ Paddling
- ❑ Rock Climbing
- ❑ Swimming
- ❑ Waterfalls
- ❑ Water sports
- ❑ Wildlife Viewing
- ❑
- ❑
- ❑
- ❑

- ❑
- ❑
- ❑
- ❑
- ❑
- ❑
- ❑
- ❑
- ❑
- ❑
- ❑

Facilities:

- ❑ ADA
- ❑ Picnic sites
- ❑ Restrooms
- ❑ Showers
- ❑ Trailer Access
- ❑ Visitor center
- ❑ Group Camping
- ❑ RV Camp
- ❑ Rustic Camping
- ❑ Cabins / Yurts
- ❑ Day Use Area

Notes:

Get the Facts

- ❑ Phone   423-257-2167
- ❑ Park Hours

  _____

- ❑ Reservations? ____Y ____N

  date made_____
- ❑ Open all year ____Y_____N

  dates_____
- ❑ Check in time _____
- ❑ Check out time _____
- ❑ Pet friendly _____Y _____N
- ❑ Max RV length _____
- ❑ Distance from home

  miles: _____

  hours: _____
- ❑ Address_____

  _____

  _____

Fees:

- ❑ Day Use $ _____
- ❑ Camp Sites $ _____
- ❑ RV Sites $ _____
- ❑ Refund policy

  _____

  _____

  _____

Make It Personal

Trip dates: _____ | The weather was: Sunny Cloudy Rainy Stormy Snowy Foggy Warm Cold

Why I went:
_____

_____

How I got there: (circle all that apply) Plane Train Car Bus Bike Hike RV MC
_____

I went with:
_____

We stayed in (space, cabin # etc):
_____

Most relaxing day:
_____

Something funny:
_____

Someone we met:
_____

Best story told:
_____

The kids liked this:
_____

The best food:
_____

Games played:
_____

Something disappointing:
_____

Next time I'll do this differently:
_____

_____

Coal Creek Miners Museum & Discovery Trail
City: Rocky Top   County: Campbell
Plan your trip: https://www.tnvacation.com/local/rocky-top-coal-creek-motor-discovery-trail

History:

Things To Do:

- ❏ ADA availability
- ❏ Public Restrooms
- ❏ Gift Shop
- ❏ Museum
- ❏ Visitor Center
- ❏ Picnic areas
- ❏ Chamber of Commerce
- ❏ Monuments
- ❏ Art Galleries
- ❏ Tours
- ❏ Street Art
- ❏ Natural Areas
- ❏ Living History
- ❏ Cemetery
- ❏ Amphitheater

Places I Want to Visit in the Area:

Restaurants:

Boutiques & Shops:

Monuments:

Museums:

Get the Facts

- ❏ Address_____
  _____
- ❏ Phone   865-457-4542
- ❏ Best season to visit
  _____
- ❏ Pet Friendly   Y   N
- ❏ Reservations?   Y   N
  date made_____
- ❏ Distance from home
  miles: _____
  hours: _____

Budget for this trip:

Parking	$
Food	$
Museums	$
Hotel	$
Shopping	$
Total	$

Notes:

Restaurant:

My Experience:

Shopping:

Best Find:

The shop I want to go back to:

Museum:

The coolest thing I learned about this area:

Other:

Sycamore Shoals
City: Elizabethton   County: Carter

Plan your trip: https://tnstateparks.com/parks/sycamore-shoals

History:

Things To Do:

- ❏ ADA availability
- ❏ Public Restrooms
- ❏ Gift Shop
- ❏ Museum
- ❏ Visitor Center
- ❏ Picnic areas
- ❏ Chamber of Commerce
- ❏ Monuments
- ❏ Art Galleries
- ❏ Tours
- ❏ Street Art
- ❏ Natural Areas
- ❏ Living History
- ❏ Cemetery
- ❏ Amphitheater

Places I Want to Visit in the Area:

Restaurants:
Boutiques & Shops:
Monuments:
Museums:

Get the Facts

- ❏ Address_____
  _____
- ❏ Phone   423-543-5808
- ❏ Best season to visit
  _____
- ❏ Pet Friendly   Y   N
- ❏ Reservations?   Y   N
  date made_____
- ❏ Distance from home
  miles: _____
  hours: _____

Budget for this trip:

Parking	$
Food	$
Museums	$
Hotel	$
Shopping	$
Total	$

Notes:

Restaurant:

My Experience:

Shopping:

Best Find:

The shop I want to go back to:

Museum:

The coolest thing I learned about this area:

Other:

Battle of Bean Station Civil War Burial Site
City: Bean Station   County: Grainger

Plan your trip: https://www.tnvacation.com/civil-war/place/206/battle-of-beans-station/

History:

Things To Do:

- ☐ ADA availability
- ☐ Public Restrooms
- ☐ Gift Shop
- ☐ Museum
- ☐ Visitor Center
- ☐ Picnic areas
- ☐ Chamber of Commerce
- ☐ Monuments
- ☐ Art Galleries
- ☐ Tours
- ☐ Street Art
- ☐ Natural Areas
- ☐ Living History
- ☐ Cemetery
- ☐ Amphitheater

Places I Want to Visit in the Area:

Restaurants:
Boutiques & Shops:
Monuments:
Museums:

Get the Facts

- ☐ Address_____

  _____

- ☐ Phone_____
- ☐ Best season to visit

  _____

- ☐ Pet Friendly   Y   N
- ☐ Reservations?   Y   N

  date made_____

- ☐ Distance from home

  miles: _____

  hours: _____

Budget for this trip:

Parking	$
Food	$
Museums	$
Hotel	$
Shopping	$
Total	$

Notes:

Restaurant:

My Experience:

Shopping:

Best Find:

The shop I want to go back to:

Museum:

The coolest thing I learned about this area:

Other:

Crockett Tavern Museum
City: Morristown   County: Hamblen

Plan your trip: http://crocketttavernmuseum.org/

History:

Get the Facts

- ❑ Address_____
  _____
- ❑ Phone   423-587-9900
- ❑ Best season to visit
  _____
- ❑ Pet Friendly   Y   N
- ❑ Reservations?   Y   N
  date made_____
- ❑ Distance from home
  miles: _____
  hours: _____

Things To Do:

- ❑ ADA availability
- ❑ Public Restrooms
- ❑ Gift Shop
- ❑ Museum
- ❑ Visitor Center
- ❑ Picnic areas
- ❑ Chamber of Commerce

- ❑ Monuments
- ❑ Art Galleries
- ❑ Tours
- ❑ Street Art
- ❑ Natural Areas
- ❑ Living History
- ❑ Cemetery
- ❑ Amphitheater

Places I Want to Visit in the Area:

Restaurants:

Boutiques & Shops:

Monuments:

Museums:

Budget for this trip:

Parking	$
Food	$
Museums	$
Hotel	$
Shopping	$
Total	$

Notes:

Restaurant:

My Experience:

Shopping:

Best Find:

The shop I want to go back to:

Museum:

The coolest thing I learned about this area:

Other:

Historic Downtown Morrisville
City: Morrisville   County: Hamblen

Plan your trip: https://downtownmorristown.city/

History:

Get the Facts
- ☐ Address_____
  _____
- ☐ Phone   423-312-1476
- ☐ Best season to visit
  _____
- ☐ Pet Friendly   Y   N
- ☐ Reservations?   Y   N
  date made_____
- ☐ Distance from home
  miles: _____
  hours: _____

Things To Do:

- ☐ ADA availability
- ☐ Public Restrooms
- ☐ Gift Shop
- ☐ Museum
- ☐ Visitor Center
- ☐ Picnic areas
- ☐ Chamber of Commerce

- ☐ Monuments
- ☐ Art Galleries
- ☐ Tours
- ☐ Street Art
- ☐ Natural Areas
- ☐ Living History
- ☐ Cemetery
- ☐ Amphitheater

Places I Want to Visit in the Area:

Restaurants:

Boutiques & Shops:

Monuments:

Museums:

Budget for this trip:

Parking	$
Food	$
Museums	$
Hotel	$
Shopping	$
Total	$

Notes:

Restaurant:

My Experience:

Shopping:

Best Find:

The shop I want to go back to:

Museum:

The coolest thing I learned about this area:

Other:

Appalachian Quilt Squares
City: *See Below   County: Various

Plan your trip http://www.vacationaqt.com/

Take a Drive – How Many Can You Find?

- ❑ Bear Paws
- ❑ Carpenter Star Variation
- ❑ Brother Scheier
- ❑ Country Star
- ❑ Compass
- ❑ Hourglass Variation
- ❑ Veterans Star
- ❑ Lakota Star
- ❑ Monkey Wrench
- ❑ Patriotic Ohio Star
- ❑ Preacher in the Box
- ❑ Drunkards Path
- ❑ Which Way North
- ❑ Mariners Compass
- ❑ Puzzle Box
- ❑ Springfield's Compass
- ❑ Square Dance
- ❑ Summer Star
- ❑ Sunflower Mural
- ❑ Sunflower
- ❑ The Duncan
- ❑ Tobacco Road
- ❑ Turkey Trot
- ❑ Twin Star
- ❑ Bright Night Star & Summer Star
- ❑ Snowball
- ❑ Double Wedding Ring
- ❑ Bow Tie
- ❑

Get the Facts

- ❑ Address_____
  _____
- ❑ Phone   870-615-2195
- ❑ Best season to visit
  _____
- ❑ Pet Friendly   Y   N
- ❑ Reservations?   Y   N
  date made_____
- ❑ Distance from home
  miles: _____
  hours: _____

Budget for this trip:

Parking	$
Food	$
Museums	$
Hotel	$
Shopping	$
Total	$

Notes: *This is a regional activity covering much of the southside and southwest of the state.

Places I Want to Visit on the Drive:

Restaurants:

Boutiques & Shops:

Monuments:

Museums:

Restaurant:

My Experience:

Shopping:

Best Find:

The shop I want to go back to:

Museum:

The coolest thing I learned about this area:

Other:

Bleak House/Confederate Memorial Hall

City: Knoxville   County: Knox

Plan your trip: https://tennesseerivervalleygeotourism.org/entries/confederate-memorial-hall-bleak-house/eb973eac-0d5e-4214-9f5d-98c507abfe87

History:

Get the Facts

❑ Address_____

_____

❑ Phone   865-585-0811

❑ Best season to visit

_____

❑ Pet Friendly   Y   N

❑ Reservations?   Y   N

date made_____

❑ Distance from home

miles: _____

hours: _____

Things To Do:

❑ ADA availability
❑ Public Restrooms
❑ Gift Shop
❑ Museum
❑ Visitor Center
❑ Picnic areas
❑ Chamber of Commerce

❑ Monuments
❑ Art Galleries
❑ Tours
❑ Street Art
❑ Natural Areas
❑ Living History
❑ Cemetery
❑ Amphitheater

Places I Want to Visit in the Area:

Restaurants:
Boutiques & Shops:
Monuments:
Museums:

Budget for this trip:

Parking	$
Food	$
Museums	$
Hotel	$
Shopping	$
Total	$

Notes:

Restaurant:

My Experience:

Shopping:

Best Find:

The shop I want to go back to:

Museum:

The coolest thing I learned about this area:

Other:

Historic Ramsey House
City: Knoxville   County: Knox
Plan your trip: http://www.ramseyhouse.org/

History:

Things To Do:

- [ ] ADA availability
- [ ] Public Restrooms
- [ ] Gift Shop
- [ ] Museum
- [ ] Visitor Center
- [ ] Picnic areas
- [ ] Chamber of Commerce
- [ ] Monuments
- [ ] Art Galleries
- [ ] Tours
- [ ] Street Art
- [ ] Natural Areas
- [ ] Living History
- [ ] Cemetery
- [ ] Amphitheater

Places I Want to Visit in the Area:

Restaurants:

Boutiques & Shops:

Monuments:

Museums:

Get the Facts

- [ ] Address_____

_____

- [ ] Phone   865-546-0745
- [ ] Best season to visit

_____

- [ ] Pet Friendly   Y   N
- [ ] Reservations?   Y   N

  date made_____

- [ ] Distance from home

  miles: _____

  hours: _____

Budget for this trip:

Parking	$
Food	$
Museums	$
Hotel	$
Shopping	$
Total	$

Notes:

Restaurant:

My Experience:

Shopping:

Best Find:

The shop I want to go back to:

Museum:

The coolest thing I learned about this area:

Other:

Marble Springs State Historic Site
City: Knoxville   County: Knox

Plan your trip: https://www.visitknoxville.com/listings/marble-springs-state-historic-site/1365/

History:

Get the Facts

- ❑ Address_____
  _____

- ❑ Phone   865-573-5508
- ❑ Best season to visit
  _____

- ❑ Pet Friendly   Y   N
- ❑ Reservations?   Y   N

  date made_____

- ❑ Distance from home

  miles: _____

  hours: _____

Things To Do:

- ❑ ADA availability
- ❑ Public Restrooms
- ❑ Gift Shop
- ❑ Museum
- ❑ Visitor Center
- ❑ Picnic areas
- ❑ Chamber of Commerce
- ❑ Monuments
- ❑ Art Galleries
- ❑ Tours
- ❑ Street Art
- ❑ Natural Areas
- ❑ Living History
- ❑ Cemetery
- ❑ Amphitheater

Places I Want to Visit in the Area:

Restaurants:

Boutiques & Shops:

Monuments:

Museums:

Budget for this trip:

Parking	$
Food	$
Museums	$
Hotel	$
Shopping	$
Total	$

Notes:

Restaurant:

My Experience:

Shopping:

Best Find:

The shop I want to go back to:

Museum:

The coolest thing I learned about this area:

Other:

William Blount Mansion
City: Knoxville   County: Knox

Plan your trip: http://blountmansion.org/

History:

Things To Do:

- [ ] ADA availability
- [ ] Public Restrooms
- [ ] Gift Shop
- [ ] Museum
- [ ] Visitor Center
- [ ] Picnic areas
- [ ] Chamber of Commerce
- [ ] Monuments
- [ ] Art Galleries
- [ ] Tours
- [ ] Street Art
- [ ] Natural Areas
- [ ] Living History
- [ ] Cemetery
- [ ] Amphitheater

Places I Want to Visit in the Area:

Restaurants:

Boutiques & Shops:

Monuments:

Museums:

Get the Facts

- [ ] Address_____
  _____
- [ ] Phone 865-525-2375 x6284
- [ ] Best season to visit
  _____
- [ ] Pet Friendly Y N
- [ ] Reservations? Y N
  date made_____
- [ ] Distance from home
  miles: _____
  hours: _____

Budget for this trip:

Parking	$
Food	$
Museums	$
Hotel	$
Shopping	$
Total	$

Notes:

Restaurant:

My Experience:

Shopping:

Best Find:

The shop I want to go back to:

Museum:

The coolest thing I learned about this area:

Other:

Fort Loudoun State Historic Park
City: Vonore   County: Monroe

Plan your trip: https://tnstateparks.com/parks/fort-loudoun

History:

Get the Facts

- ☐ Address_____

  _____

- ☐ Phone   423-420-2331
- ☐ Best season to visit

  _____

- ☐ Pet Friendly   Y   N
- ☐ Reservations?   Y   N

  date made_____

- ☐ Distance from home

  miles: _____

  hours: _____

Things To Do:

- ☐ ADA availability
- ☐ Public Restrooms
- ☐ Gift Shop
- ☐ Museum
- ☐ Visitor Center
- ☐ Picnic areas
- ☐ Chamber of Commerce
- ☐ Monuments
- ☐ Art Galleries
- ☐ Tours
- ☐ Street Art
- ☐ Natural Areas
- ☐ Living History
- ☐ Cemetery
- ☐ Amphitheater

Places I Want to Visit in the Area:

Restaurants:

Boutiques & Shops:

Monuments:

Museums:

Budget for this trip:

Parking	$
Food	$
Museums	$
Hotel	$
Shopping	$
Total	$

Notes:

Restaurant:

My Experience:

Shopping:

Best Find:

The shop I want to go back to:

Museum:

The coolest thing I learned about this area:

Other:

X-10 Reactor, Oak Ridge National Laboratory
City: Oak Ridge   County: Roane

Plan your trip: https://www.energy.gov/management/x-10-graphite-reactor

History:

Get the Facts

- ❑ Address_____
  _____
- ❑ Phone   202-586-2550
- ❑ Best season to visit
  _____
- ❑ Pet Friendly   Y   N
- ❑ Reservations?   Y   N
  date made_____
- ❑ Distance from home
  miles: _____
  hours: _____

Things To Do:

- ❑ ADA availability
- ❑ Public Restrooms
- ❑ Gift Shop
- ❑ Museum
- ❑ Visitor Center
- ❑ Picnic areas
- ❑ Chamber of Commerce
- ❑ Monuments
- ❑ Art Galleries
- ❑ Tours
- ❑ Street Art
- ❑ Natural Areas
- ❑ Living History
- ❑ Cemetery
- ❑ Amphitheater

Places I Want to Visit in the Area:

Restaurants:

Boutiques & Shops:

Monuments:

Museums:

Budget for this trip:

Parking	$
Food	$
Museums	$
Hotel	$
Shopping	$
Total	$

Notes:

Restaurant:

My Experience:

Shopping:

Best Find:

The shop I want to go back to:

Museum:

The coolest thing I learned about this area:

Other:

The Old Mill
City: Pigeon Forge   County: Sevier
Plan your trip: https://old-mill.com/

History:

Get the Facts

- ❑ Address_____

  _____

- ❑ Phone   877-653-6455
- ❑ Best season to visit

  _____

- ❑ Pet Friendly   Y   N
- ❑ Reservations?   Y   N

  date made_____

- ❑ Distance from home

  miles: _____

  hours: _____

Things To Do:

- ❑ ADA availability
- ❑ Public Restrooms
- ❑ Gift Shop
- ❑ Museum
- ❑ Visitor Center
- ❑ Picnic areas
- ❑ Chamber of Commerce
- ❑ Monuments
- ❑ Art Galleries
- ❑ Tours
- ❑ Street Art
- ❑ Natural Areas
- ❑ Living History
- ❑ Cemetery
- ❑ Amphitheater

Places I Want to Visit in the Area:

Restaurants:

Boutiques & Shops:

Monuments:

Museums:

Budget for this trip:

Parking	$
Food	$
Museums	$
Hotel	$
Shopping	$
Total	$

Notes:

Restaurant:

My Experience:

Shopping:

Best Find:

The shop I want to go back to:

Museum:

The coolest thing I learned about this area:

Other:

*National Home for Disabled Volunteer Soldiers

City: Johnson City   County: Washington

Plan your trip: https://www.nps.gov/places/mountain-branch-mountain-home-tennessee.htm

History:

Things To Do:

- ☐ ADA availability
- ☐ Public Restrooms
- ☐ Gift Shop
- ☐ Museum
- ☐ Visitor Center
- ☐ Picnic areas
- ☐ Chamber of Commerce

- ☐ Monuments
- ☐ Art Galleries
- ☐ Tours
- ☐ Street Art
- ☐ Natural Areas
- ☐ Living History
- ☐ Cemetery
- ☐ Amphitheater

Places I Want to Visit in the Area:

Restaurants:

Boutiques & Shops:

Monuments:

Museums:

Get the Facts

- ☐ Address_____

  _____

- ☐ Phone   423-439-8069
- ☐ Best season to visit

  _____

- ☐ Pet Friendly   Y   N
- ☐ Reservations?   Y   N

  date made_____

- ☐ Distance from home

  miles: _____

  hours: _____

Budget for this trip:

Parking	$
Food	$
Museums	$
Hotel	$
Shopping	$
Total	$

Notes:
*Mountain Branch

Restaurant:

My Experience:

Shopping:

Best Find:

The shop I want to go back to:

Museum:

The coolest thing I learned about this area:

Other:

Museum of Appalachia
City: Clinton   County: Anderson

Plan your trip: https://www.museumofappalachia.org/

Activities:

- ❑ Biking
- ❑ Birding
- ❑ Boating
- ❑ Caving
- ❑ Disc Golf / Golf
- ❑ Fishing
- ❑ Hiking
- ❑ Hunting
- ❑ Paddling
- ❑ Rock Climbing
- ❑ Swimming
- ❑ Tours
- ❑ Watersports
- ❑ Wildlife Viewing
- ❑
- ❑
- ❑
- ❑
- ❑
- ❑
- ❑
- ❑
- ❑
- ❑

Facilities:

- ❑ ADA
- ❑ Gift Shop
- ❑ Museum
- ❑ Visitor Center
- ❑ Picnic sites
- ❑ Restrooms
- ❑
- ❑
- ❑
- ❑
- ❑
- ❑

Things to do in the area:

Get the Facts

- ❑ Phone 865-494-7680
- ❑ Park Hours

_____

- ❑ Reservations? ____Y ____N

date made_____

- ❑ Open all year? ____Y____N

dates_____

- ❑ Dog friendly _____Y _____N
- ❑ Distance from home

miles: _____

hours: _____

- ❑ Address_____

_____

_____

Fees:

- ❑ Day Use $ _____
- ❑ Refund policy

_____

_____

_____

Notes:

Tuckaleechee Caverns
City: Townsend   County: Blount

Plan your trip: https://tuckaleecheecaverns.com/

Activities:

- ❑ Biking
- ❑ Birding
- ❑ Boating
- ❑ Caving
- ❑ Disc Golf / Golf
- ❑ Fishing
- ❑ Hiking
- ❑ Hunting
- ❑ Paddling
- ❑ Rock Climbing
- ❑ Swimming
- ❑ Tours
- ❑ Watersports
- ❑ Wildlife Viewing
- ❑
- ❑
- ❑
- ❑
- ❑
- ❑
- ❑
- ❑
- ❑

Facilities:

- ❑ ADA
- ❑ Gift Shop
- ❑ Museum
- ❑ Visitor Center
- ❑ Picnic sites
- ❑ Restrooms
- ❑
- ❑
- ❑
- ❑
- ❑
- ❑

Things to do in the area:

Get the Facts

- ❑ Phone 865-448-2274
- ❑ Park Hours

  _____

- ❑ Reservations? ____Y ____N

  date made_____

- ❑ Open all year? ____Y____N

  dates_____

- ❑ Dog friendly _____Y _____N

- ❑ Distance from home

  miles: _____

  hours: _____

- ❑ Address_____

  _____

  _____

Fees:

- ❑ Day Use $ _____
- ❑ Refund policy

  _____

  _____

  _____

Notes:

Sycamore Shoals State Historic Area
City: Elizabethton   County: Carter

Plan your trip: https://tnstateparks.com/parks/sycamore-shoals

Activities:

- ❑ Biking
- ❑ Birding
- ❑ Boating
- ❑ Caving
- ❑ Disc Golf / Golf
- ❑ Fishing
- ❑ Hiking
- ❑ Hunting
- ❑ Paddling
- ❑ Rock Climbing
- ❑ Swimming
- ❑ Tours
- ❑ Watersports
- ❑ Wildlife Viewing
- ❑
- ❑
- ❑
- ❑
- ❑
- ❑
- ❑
- ❑
- ❑
- ❑

Facilities:

- ❑ ADA
- ❑ Gift Shop
- ❑ Museum
- ❑ Visitor Center
- ❑ Picnic sites
- ❑ Restrooms
- ❑
- ❑
- ❑
- ❑
- ❑
- ❑

Things to do in the area:

Get the Facts

- ❑ Phone 423-543-5808
- ❑ Park Hours

  _____

- ❑ Reservations? ____Y ____N

  date made_____

- ❑ Open all year? ____Y____N

  dates_____

- ❑ Dog friendly ____Y ____N

- ❑ Distance from home

  miles: _____

  hours: _____

- ❑ Address_____

  _____

  _____

Fees:

- ❑ Day Use $ _____
- ❑ Refund policy

  _____

  _____

  _____

Notes:

Swaggerty Fort Historic Site
City: Parrotsville   County: Cocke

Plan your trip: https://www.yallvisitthesmokies.com/attraction/swaggerty-fort/

Activities:

- ❏ Biking
- ❏ Birding
- ❏ Boating
- ❏ Caving
- ❏ Disc Golf / Golf
- ❏ Fishing
- ❏ Hiking
- ❏ Hunting
- ❏ Paddling
- ❏ Rock Climbing
- ❏ Swimming
- ❏ Tours

- ❏ Watersports
- ❏ Wildlife Viewing
- ❏
- ❏
- ❏
- ❏
- ❏
- ❏
- ❏
- ❏
- ❏
- ❏

Facilities:

- ❏ ADA
- ❏ Gift Shop
- ❏ Museum
- ❏ Visitor Center
- ❏ Picnic sites
- ❏ Restrooms

- ❏
- ❏
- ❏
- ❏
- ❏
- ❏

Things to do in the area:

Get the Facts

- ❏ Phone 423-625-9675
- ❏ Park Hours

_____

- ❏ Reservations? ____Y ____N

date made_____

- ❏ Open all year? ____Y____N

dates_____

- ❏ Dog friendly _____Y _____N
- ❏ Distance from home

miles: _____

hours: _____

- ❏ Address_____

_____

_____

Fees:

- ❏ Day Use $ _____
- ❏ Refund policy

_____

_____

_____

Notes:

Fort Dickerson Park
City: Knoxville   County: Knox

Plan your trip: https://outdoorknoxville.com/places/parks/south/fort-dickerson-park/

Activities:

- ❑ Biking
- ❑ Birding
- ❑ Boating
- ❑ Caving
- ❑ Disc Golf / Golf
- ❑ Fishing
- ❑ Hiking
- ❑ Hunting
- ❑ Paddling
- ❑ Rock Climbing
- ❑ Swimming
- ❑ Tours

- ❑ Watersports
- ❑ Wildlife Viewing
- ❑
- ❑
- ❑
- ❑
- ❑
- ❑
- ❑
- ❑
- ❑
- ❑

Facilities:

- ❑ ADA
- ❑ Gift Shop
- ❑ Museum
- ❑ Visitor Center
- ❑ Picnic sites
- ❑ Restrooms

- ❑
- ❑
- ❑
- ❑
- ❑
- ❑

Things to do in the area:

Get the Facts

- ❑ Phone 865-215-4311
- ❑ Park Hours

  _____

- ❑ Reservations? ____Y ____N

  date made_____

- ❑ Open all year? ____Y____N

  dates_____

- ❑ Dog friendly _____Y _____N

- ❑ Distance from home

  miles: _____

  hours: _____

- ❑ Address_____

  _____

  _____

Fees:

- ❑ Day Use $ _____
- ❑ Refund policy

  _____

  _____

  _____

Notes:

James White's Fort
City: Knoxville   County: Knox

Plan your trip: https://www.jameswhitesfort.org/

Activities:

- ☐ Biking
- ☐ Birding
- ☐ Boating
- ☐ Caving
- ☐ Disc Golf / Golf
- ☐ Fishing
- ☐ Hiking
- ☐ Hunting
- ☐ Paddling
- ☐ Rock Climbing
- ☐ Swimming
- ☐ Tours

- ☐ Watersports
- ☐ Wildlife Viewing
- ☐
- ☐
- ☐
- ☐
- ☐
- ☐
- ☐
- ☐
- ☐
- ☐

Facilities:

- ☐ ADA
- ☐ Gift Shop
- ☐ Museum
- ☐ Visitor Center
- ☐ Picnic sites
- ☐ Restrooms

- ☐
- ☐
- ☐
- ☐
- ☐
- ☐

Things to do in the area:

Get the Facts

- ☐ Phone 865-525-6514
- ☐ Park Hours

  _____

- ☐ Reservations? ____Y ____N

  date made_____

- ☐ Open all year? ____Y____N

  dates_____

- ☐ Dog friendly _____Y _____N
- ☐ Distance from home

  miles: _____

  hours: _____

- ☐ Address_____

  _____

  _____

Fees:

- ☐ Day Use $ _____
- ☐ Refund policy

  _____

  _____

  _____

Notes:

Fort Loudoun State Park

City: Vonore   County: Monroe

Plan your trip: https://tnstateparks.com/parks/fort-loudoun

Activities:

- ❑ Biking
- ❑ Birding
- ❑ Boating
- ❑ Caving
- ❑ Disc Golf / Golf
- ❑ Fishing
- ❑ Hiking
- ❑ Hunting
- ❑ Paddling
- ❑ Rock Climbing
- ❑ Swimming
- ❑ Tours

- ❑ Watersports
- ❑ Wildlife Viewing
- ❑
- ❑
- ❑
- ❑
- ❑
- ❑
- ❑
- ❑
- ❑
- ❑

Facilities:

- ❑ ADA
- ❑ Gift Shop
- ❑ Museum
- ❑ Visitor Center
- ❑ Picnic sites
- ❑ Restrooms

- ❑
- ❑
- ❑
- ❑
- ❑
- ❑

Things to do in the area:

Get the Facts

- ❑ Phone   423-420-2331
- ❑ Park Hours

_____

- ❑ Reservations? ____Y ____N

date made_____

- ❑ Open all year? ____Y____N

dates_____

- ❑ Dog friendly _____Y _____N
- ❑ Distance from home

miles: _____

hours: _____

- ❑ Address_____

_____

_____

Fees:

- ❑ Day Use $ _____
- ❑ Refund policy

_____

_____

_____

Notes:

Rugby Natural Area
City: Rugby　　　　　County: Morgan

Plan your trip: https://www.tn.gov/twra/wildlife/viewing-area/east-tennessee/rugby-sna.html

Activities:

- ❑ Biking
- ❑ Birding
- ❑ Boating
- ❑ Caving
- ❑ Disc Golf / Golf
- ❑ Fishing
- ❑ Hiking
- ❑ Hunting
- ❑ Paddling
- ❑ Rock Climbing
- ❑ Swimming
- ❑ Tours

- ❑ Watersports
- ❑ Wildlife Viewing
- ❑
- ❑
- ❑
- ❑
- ❑
- ❑
- ❑
- ❑
- ❑
- ❑

Facilities:

- ❑ ADA
- ❑ Gift Shop
- ❑ Museum
- ❑ Visitor Center
- ❑ Picnic sites
- ❑ Restrooms

- ❑
- ❑
- ❑
- ❑
- ❑
- ❑

Things to do in the area:

Get the Facts

- ❑ Phone
- ❑ Park Hours

_____

- ❑ Reservations? ____Y ____N

  date made_____

- ❑ Open all year? ____Y____N

  dates_____

- ❑ Dog friendly _____Y _____N

- ❑ Distance from home

  miles: _____

  hours: _____

- ❑ Address_____

  _____

  _____

Fees:

- ❑ Day Use $ _____
- ❑ Refund policy

  _____

  _____

  _____

Notes:

Seven Islands State Birding Park
City: Kodak   County: Sevier

Plan your trip: https://tnstateparks.com/parks/seven-islands

Activities:

- ❑ Biking
- ❑ Birding
- ❑ Boating
- ❑ Caving
- ❑ Disc Golf / Golf
- ❑ Fishing
- ❑ Hiking
- ❑ Hunting
- ❑ Paddling
- ❑ Rock Climbing
- ❑ Swimming
- ❑ Tours

- ❑ Watersports
- ❑ Wildlife Viewing
- ❑
- ❑
- ❑
- ❑
- ❑
- ❑
- ❑
- ❑
- ❑
- ❑

Facilities:

- ❑ ADA
- ❑ Gift Shop
- ❑ Museum
- ❑ Visitor Center
- ❑ Picnic sites
- ❑ Restrooms

- ❑
- ❑
- ❑
- ❑
- ❑
- ❑

Things to do in the area:

Get the Facts

- ❑ Phone 865-407-8335
- ❑ Park Hours

_____

- ❑ Reservations? ____Y ____N

  date made_____

- ❑ Open all year? ____Y____N

  dates_____

- ❑ Dog friendly _____Y _____N

- ❑ Distance from home

  miles: _____

  hours: _____

- ❑ Address_____

  _____

  _____

Fees:

- ❑ Day Use $ _____
- ❑ Refund policy

  _____

  _____

  _____

Notes:

Rocky Fork State Park
City: Pigeon Forge   County: Sevier

Plan your trip: https://old-mill.com/

Activities:

- ❑ Biking
- ❑ Birding
- ❑ Boating
- ❑ Caving
- ❑ Disc Golf / Golf
- ❑ Fishing
- ❑ Hiking
- ❑ Hunting
- ❑ Paddling
- ❑ Rock Climbing
- ❑ Swimming
- ❑ Tours

- ❑ Watersports
- ❑ Wildlife Viewing
- ❑
- ❑
- ❑
- ❑
- ❑
- ❑
- ❑
- ❑
- ❑
- ❑

Facilities:

- ❑ ADA
- ❑ Gift Shop
- ❑ Museum
- ❑ Visitor Center
- ❑ Picnic sites
- ❑ Restrooms

- ❑
- ❑
- ❑
- ❑
- ❑
- ❑

Things to do in the area:

Get the Facts

- ❑ Phone 877-653-6455
- ❑ Park Hours

  _____

- ❑ Reservations? ____Y ____N

  date made_____

- ❑ Open all year? ____Y____N

  dates_____

- ❑ Dog friendly _____Y _____N

- ❑ Distance from home

  miles: _____

  hours: _____

- ❑ Address_____

  _____

  _____

Fees:

- ❑ Day Use $ _____
- ❑ Refund policy

  _____

  _____

  _____

Notes:

Notes:

National Wildlife Refuges in Tennessee

There are 7 National Wildlife Refuges in Tennessee.
Why not add these to your bucket list?

- ❑ Chicksaw National Wildlife Refuge
- ❑ Cross Creeks National Wildlife Refuge
- ❑ Hatchie National Wildlife Refuge
- ❑ Lake Isom National Wildlife Refuge
- ❑ Lower Hatchie National Wildlife Refuge
- ❑ Reelfoot National Wildlife Refuge
- ❑ Tennessee National Wildlife Refuge

Ultimate Tennessee Road Trip

- ❑ Andrew Jackson's Hermitage: Home of the People's President
- ❑ President James K. Polk Home & Museum
- ❑ Alex Haley Museum & Interpretive Center
- ❑ Loretta Lynn's Ranch
- ❑ Andrew Johnson National Historic Site
- ❑ Elvis Presley's Graceland
- ❑ Carnton
- ❑ Fort Pillow State Historic Park
- ❑ Chickamauga & Chattanooga National Military Park
- ❑ Stones River National Battlefield
- ❑ Shiloh National Military Park
- ❑ Fort Donelson National Battlefield
- ❑ Parkers Crossroads Battlefield
- ❑ Tennessee State Museum
- ❑ Sergeant Alvin C. York State Historic Park
- ❑ West Tennessee Agricultural Museum

- ❑ Museum of East Tennessee History
- ❑ Pink Palace Museum
- ❑ Sequoyah Birthplace Museum
- ❑ Pinson Mounds State Archaeological Park
- ❑ Red Clay State Historic Park
- ❑ Wynnwood State Historic Site
- ❑ Green McAdoo Cultural Center
- ❑ National Civil Rights Museum
- ❑ Fisk University
- ❑ Griggs Hall and American Baptist College
- ❑ Beale Street Historic District
- ❑ Museum of Appalachia
- ❑ Historic Collinsville
- ❑ Dolly Parton Statue
- ❑ Days Gone By Museum
- ❑ Rocky Mount Museum
- ❑ National Medal of Honor Heritage Center

To learn more visit: https://www.tnvacation.com/articles/ultimate-tennessee-road-trip-history-buffs

Name:

City: County:

Plan your trip:

Activities:

- ❑ Archery
- ❑ Backpacking
- ❑ Biking Trails
- ❑ Boating
- ❑ Fishing
- ❑ Hiking
- ❑ Horseback
- ❑ Hunting
- ❑ Ice Fishing
- ❑ Mountain Bike
- ❑ OHV
- ❑ Photography

- ❑ Rock Climbing ❑
- ❑ Sailing ❑
- ❑ Skiing ❑
- ❑ Stargazing ❑
- ❑ Swimming ❑
- ❑ Water sports ❑
- ❑ Wildlife & ❑
  Birding ❑
- ❑ ❑
- ❑ ❑
- ❑ ❑
- ❑ ❑

Facilities:

- ❑ ADA
- ❑ Historic Sites
- ❑ Picnic sites
- ❑ Restrooms
- ❑ Showers
- ❑ Visitor center
- ❑ RV Camp
- ❑ Tent Camp
- ❑ Primitive Camp
- ❑ Cabins / Yurts
- ❑ Day Use Area

Notes:

Get the Facts

- ❑ Phone
- ❑ Park Hours

  _____

- ❑ Reservations? ____Y ____N

  date made_____
- ❑ Open all year ____Y____N

  dates_____
- ❑ Check in time _____
- ❑ Check out time _____
- ❑ Dog friendly _____Y _____N
- ❑ Max RV length _____
- ❑ Distance from home

  miles: _____

  hours: _____
- ❑ Address_____

  _____

  _____

Fees:

- ❑ Day Use $ _____
- ❑ Camp Sites $ _____
- ❑ RV Sites $ _____
- ❑ Refund policy

  _____

  _____

  _____

Make It Personal

Trip dates:

The weather was: Sunny Cloudy Rainy Stormy Snowy Foggy Warm Cold

Why I went:

How I got there: (circle all that apply) Plane Train Car Bus Bike Hike RV MC

I went with:

We stayed in (space, cabin # etc):

Most relaxing day:

Something funny:

Someone we met:

Best story told:

The kids liked this:

The best food:

Games played:

Something disappointing:

Next time I'll do this differently:

Name:

City: County:

Plan your trip:

Activities:

- ❑ Archery
- ❑ Backpacking
- ❑ Biking Trails
- ❑ Boating
- ❑ Fishing
- ❑ Hiking
- ❑ Horseback
- ❑ Hunting
- ❑ Ice Fishing ❑
- ❑ Mountain Bike ❑
- ❑ OHV ❑
- ❑ Photography ❑

- ❑ Rock Climbing ❑
- ❑ Sailing ❑
- ❑ Skiing ❑
- ❑ Stargazing ❑
- ❑ Swimming ❑
- ❑ Water sports ❑
- ❑ Wildlife & ❑
-     Birding ❑
- ❑
- ❑
- ❑
- ❑

Facilities:

- ❑ ADA
- ❑ Historic Sites
- ❑ Picnic sites
- ❑ Restrooms
- ❑ Showers
- ❑ Visitor center
- ❑ RV Camp
- ❑ Tent Camp
- ❑ Primitive Camp
- ❑ Cabins / Yurts
- ❑ Day Use Area

Notes:

Get the Facts

- ❑ Phone
- ❑ Park Hours

  _____

- ❑ Reservations? ____Y ____N

  date made_____

- ❑ Open all year ____Y____N

  dates_____

- ❑ Check in time _____
- ❑ Check out time _____
- ❑ Dog friendly _____Y _____N
- ❑ Max RV length _____
- ❑ Distance from home

  miles: _____

  hours: _____

- ❑ Address_____

  _____

  _____

Fees:

- ❑ Day Use $ _____
- ❑ Camp Sites $ _____
- ❑ RV Sites $ _____
- ❑ Refund policy

  _____

  _____

  _____

Make It Personal

Trip dates:

The weather was: Sunny Cloudy Rainy Stormy Snowy Foggy Warm Cold

Why I went:

How I got there: (circle all that apply) Plane Train Car Bus Bike Hike RV MC

I went with:

We stayed in (space, cabin # etc):

Most relaxing day:

Something funny:

Someone we met:

Best story told:

The kids liked this:

The best food:

Games played:

Something disappointing:

Next time I'll do this differently:

Name:

City: County:

Plan your trip:

Activities:

- ❑ Archery
- ❑ Backpacking
- ❑ Biking Trails
- ❑ Boating
- ❑ Fishing
- ❑ Hiking
- ❑ Horseback
- ❑ Hunting
- ❑ Ice Fishing
- ❑ Mountain Bike
- ❑ OHV
- ❑ Photography

- ❑ Rock Climbing ❑
- ❑ Sailing   ❑
- ❑ Skiing   ❑
- ❑ Stargazing   ❑
- ❑ Swimming   ❑
- ❑ Water sports ❑
- ❑ Wildlife & ❑
-      Birding
- ❑   ❑
- ❑   ❑
- ❑   ❑
- ❑   ❑

Facilities:

- ❑ ADA
- ❑ Historic Sites
- ❑ Picnic sites
- ❑ Restrooms
- ❑ Showers
- ❑ Visitor center
- ❑ RV Camp
- ❑ Tent Camp
- ❑ Primitive Camp
- ❑ Cabins / Yurts
- ❑ Day Use Area

Notes:

Get the Facts

- ❑ Phone
- ❑ Park Hours

  _____

- ❑ Reservations? ____Y ____N

  date made_____
- ❑ Open all year ____Y____N

  dates_____
- ❑ Check in time _____
- ❑ Check out time _____
- ❑ Dog friendly _____Y _____N
- ❑ Max RV length _____
- ❑ Distance from home

  miles: _____

  hours: _____
- ❑ Address_____

  _____

  _____

Fees:

- ❑ Day Use $ _____
- ❑ Camp Sites $ _____
- ❑ RV Sites $ _____
- ❑ Refund policy

  _____

  _____

  _____

Make It Personal

Trip dates: _____ | The weather was: Sunny Cloudy Rainy Stormy Snowy Foggy Warm Cold

Why I went: _____

_____

How I got there: (circle all that apply) Plane Train Car Bus Bike Hike RV MC

I went with: _____

We stayed in (space, cabin # etc): _____

Most relaxing day: _____

_____

Something funny: _____

_____

Someone we met: _____

_____

Best story told: _____

_____

The kids liked this: _____

_____

The best food: _____

_____

Games played: _____

_____

Something disappointing: _____

_____

Next time I'll do this differently: _____

_____

Name:

City: County:

Plan your trip:

Activities:

- ☐ Archery
- ☐ Backpacking
- ☐ Biking Trails
- ☐ Boating
- ☐ Fishing
- ☐ Hiking
- ☐ Horseback
- ☐ Hunting
- ☐ Ice Fishing
- ☐ Mountain Bike
- ☐ OHV
- ☐ Photography

- ☐ Rock Climbing ☐
- ☐ Sailing ☐
- ☐ Skiing ☐
- ☐ Stargazing ☐
- ☐ Swimming ☐
- ☐ Water sports ☐
- ☐ Wildlife & ☐
- Birding ☐
- ☐ ☐
- ☐ ☐
- ☐ ☐
- ☐ ☐

Facilities:

- ☐ ADA
- ☐ Historic Sites
- ☐ Picnic sites
- ☐ Restrooms
- ☐ Showers
- ☐ Visitor center
- ☐ RV Camp
- ☐ Tent Camp
- ☐ Primitive Camp
- ☐ Cabins / Yurts
- ☐ Day Use Area

Notes:

Get the Facts

- ☐ Phone
- ☐ Park Hours

  _____

- ☐ Reservations? ____Y ____N

  date made_____
- ☐ Open all year ____Y_____N

  dates_____
- ☐ Check in time _____
- ☐ Check out time _____
- ☐ Dog friendly _____Y _____N
- ☐ Max RV length _____
- ☐ Distance from home

  miles: _____

  hours: _____
- ☐ Address_____

  _____

  _____

Fees:

- ☐ Day Use $ _____
- ☐ Camp Sites $ _____
- ☐ RV Sites $ _____
- ☐ Refund policy

  _____

  _____

  _____

Make It Personal

Trip dates: | The weather was: Sunny Cloudy Rainy Stormy Snowy Foggy Warm Cold

Why I went:

_____

How I got there: (circle all that apply)   Plane   Train   Car   Bus   Bike   Hike   RV   MC

I went with:

We stayed in (space, cabin # etc):

Most relaxing day:

_____

Something funny:

_____

Someone we met:

_____

Best story told:

_____

The kids liked this:

_____

The best food:

_____

Games played:

_____

Something disappointing:

_____

Next time I'll do this differently:

_____

Name:

City: ## County:

Plan your trip:

Activities:

- ❑ Archery
- ❑ Backpacking
- ❑ Biking Trails
- ❑ Boating
- ❑ Fishing
- ❑ Hiking
- ❑ Horseback
- ❑ Hunting
- ❑ Ice Fishing
- ❑ Mountain Bike
- ❑ OHV
- ❑ Photography

- ❑ Rock Climbing ❑
- ❑ Sailing ❑
- ❑ Skiing ❑
- ❑ Stargazing ❑
- ❑ Swimming ❑
- ❑ Water sports ❑
- ❑ Wildlife & ❑
  Birding ❑
- ❑ ❑
- ❑ ❑
- ❑ ❑
- ❑ ❑

Facilities:

- ❑ ADA
- ❑ Historic Sites
- ❑ Picnic sites
- ❑ Restrooms
- ❑ Showers
- ❑ Visitor center
- ❑ RV Camp
- ❑ Tent Camp
- ❑ Primitive Camp
- ❑ Cabins / Yurts
- ❑ Day Use Area

Notes:

Get the Facts

- ❑ Phone
- ❑ Park Hours

  _____

- ❑ Reservations? ____Y ____N

  date made_____

- ❑ Open all year ____Y____N

  dates_____

- ❑ Check in time _____
- ❑ Check out time _____
- ❑ Dog friendly _____Y _____N
- ❑ Max RV length _____
- ❑ Distance from home

  miles: _____

  hours: _____

- ❑ Address_____

  _____

  _____

Fees:

- ❑ Day Use $ _____
- ❑ Camp Sites $ _____
- ❑ RV Sites $ _____
- ❑ Refund policy

  _____

  _____

  _____

Make It Personal

Trip dates:

The weather was: Sunny Cloudy Rainy Stormy Snowy Foggy Warm Cold

Why I went:

How I got there: (circle all that apply)   Plane   Train   Car   Bus   Bike   Hike   RV   MC

I went with:

We stayed in (space, cabin # etc):

Most relaxing day:

Something funny:

Someone we met:

Best story told:

The kids liked this:

The best food:

Games played:

Something disappointing:

Next time I'll do this differently:

Name:
City: County:
Plan your trip:

Activities:

- ❑ ATV / OHV   ❑
- ❑ Bike Trails   ❑
- ❑ Birding   ❑
- ❑ Boating   ❑
- ❑ Fishing   ❑
- ❑ Hiking   ❑
- ❑ Horseback   ❑
- ❑ Mountain Biking   ❑
- ❑ Watersports   ❑
- ❑ Wildlife   ❑
- ❑ Winter Sports

Facilities:

- ❑ ADA   ❑
- ❑ Gift Shop   ❑
- ❑ Museum   ❑
- ❑ Visitor Center   ❑
- ❑ Picnic sites   ❑
- ❑ Restrooms   ❑

Things to do in the area:

Get the Facts

- ❑ Phone
- ❑ Park Hours

  _____

- ❑ Reservations? ____Y ____N

  date made_____

- ❑ Open all year? ____Y____N

  dates_____

- ❑ Dog friendly _____Y _____N

- ❑ Distance from home

  miles: _____

  hours: _____

- ❑ Address_____

  _____

  _____

Fees:

- ❑ Day Use $ _____
- ❑ Refund policy

  _____

  _____

  _____

Notes:

Name:
City: ## County:
Plan your trip:

Activities:

- [ ] ATV / OHV   - [ ]
- [ ] Bike Trails   - [ ]
- [ ] Birding   - [ ]
- [ ] Boating   - [ ]
- [ ] Fishing   - [ ]
- [ ] Hiking   - [ ]
- [ ] Horseback   - [ ]
- [ ] Mountain Biking   - [ ]
- [ ] Watersports   - [ ]
- [ ] Wildlife   - [ ]
- [ ] Winter Sports

Facilities:

- [ ] ADA   - [ ]
- [ ] Gift Shop   - [ ]
- [ ] Museum   - [ ]
- [ ] Visitor Center   - [ ]
- [ ] Picnic sites   - [ ]
- [ ] Restrooms   - [ ]

Things to do in the area:

Get the Facts

- [ ] Phone
- [ ] Park Hours

  _____

- [ ] Reservations? ____Y ____N

  date made_____

- [ ] Open all year? ____Y____N

  dates_____

- [ ] Dog friendly _____Y _____N

- [ ] Distance from home

  miles: _____

  hours: _____

- [ ] Address_____

  _____

  _____

Fees:

- [ ] Day Use $ _____
- [ ] Refund policy

  _____

  _____

  _____

Notes:

Name:

City: **County:**

Plan your trip:

Activities:

- ❑ ATV / OHV   ❑
- ❑ Bike Trails   ❑
- ❑ Birding   ❑
- ❑ Boating   ❑
- ❑ Fishing   ❑
- ❑ Hiking   ❑
- ❑ Horseback   ❑
- ❑ Mountain Biking   ❑
- ❑ Watersports   ❑
- ❑ Wildlife   ❑
- ❑ Winter Sports

Facilities:

- ❑ ADA   ❑
- ❑ Gift Shop   ❑
- ❑ Museum   ❑
- ❑ Visitor Center   ❑
- ❑ Picnic sites   ❑
- ❑ Restrooms   ❑

Things to do in the area:

Get the Facts

- ❑ Phone
- ❑ Park Hours

_____

- ❑ Reservations? ____Y ____N

date made_____

- ❑ Open all year? ____Y____N

dates_____

- ❑ Dog friendly _____Y _____N
- ❑ Distance from home

miles: _____

hours: _____

- ❑ Address_____

_____

_____

Fees:

- ❑ Day Use $ _____
- ❑ Refund policy

_____

_____

_____

Notes:

Name:

City: County:

Plan your trip:

Activities:		**Get the Facts**

Activities:

- ❏ ATV / OHV   ❏
- ❏ Bike Trails   ❏
- ❏ Birding   ❏
- ❏ Boating   ❏
- ❏ Fishing   ❏
- ❏ Hiking   ❏
- ❏ Horseback   ❏
- ❏ Mountain Biking   ❏
- ❏ Watersports   ❏
- ❏ Wildlife   ❏
- ❏ Winter Sports

Facilities:

- ❏ ADA   ❏
- ❏ Gift Shop   ❏
- ❏ Museum   ❏
- ❏ Visitor Center   ❏
- ❏ Picnic sites   ❏
- ❏ Restrooms   ❏

Things to do in the area:

Get the Facts

- ❏ Phone
- ❏ Park Hours

_____

- ❏ Reservations? ____Y ____N

  date made_____

- ❏ Open all year? ____Y____N

  dates_____

- ❏ Dog friendly _____Y _____N

- ❏ Distance from home

  miles: _____

  hours: _____

- ❏ Address_____

  _____

  _____

Fees:

- ❏ Day Use $ _____
- ❏ Refund policy

  _____

  _____

  _____

Notes:

Name:

City: ## County:

Plan your trip:

Activities:

- ❏ ATV / OHV   ❏
- ❏ Bike Trails   ❏
- ❏ Birding   ❏
- ❏ Boating   ❏
- ❏ Fishing   ❏
- ❏ Hiking   ❏
- ❏ Horseback   ❏
- ❏ Mountain Biking   ❏
- ❏ Watersports   ❏
- ❏ Wildlife   ❏
- ❏ Winter Sports

Facilities:

- ❏ ADA   ❏
- ❏ Gift Shop   ❏
- ❏ Museum   ❏
- ❏ Visitor Center   ❏
- ❏ Picnic sites   ❏
- ❏ Restrooms   ❏

Things to do in the area:

Get the Facts

- ❏ Phone
- ❏ Park Hours

_____

- ❏ Reservations? ____Y ____N

  date made_____

- ❏ Open all year? ____Y____N

  dates_____

- ❏ Dog friendly _____Y _____N

- ❏ Distance from home

  miles: _____

  hours: _____

- ❏ Address_____

  _____

  _____

Fees:

- ❏ Day Use $ _____
- ❏ Refund policy

  _____

  _____

  _____

Notes:

Historic Areas

City: County:

Plan your trip:

History:

Things To Do:

- ❑ ADA availability
- ❑ Public Restrooms
- ❑ Gift Shop
- ❑ Museum
- ❑ Visitor Center
- ❑ Picnic areas
- ❑ Chamber of Commerce

- ❑ Monuments
- ❑ Art Galleries
- ❑ Tours
- ❑ Street Art
- ❑ Natural Areas
- ❑ Living History
- ❑ Cemetery
- ❑ Amphitheater

Places I Want to Visit in the Area:

Restaurants:

Boutiques & Shops:

Monuments:

Museums:

Get the Facts

- ❑ Address_____

  _____

- ❑ Phone
- ❑ Best season to visit

  _____

- ❑ Pet Friendly   Y   N
- ❑ Reservations?   Y   N

  date made_____

- ❑ Distance from home

  miles: _____

  hours: _____

Budget for this trip:

Parking	$
Food	$
Museums	$
Hotel	$
Shopping	$
Total	$

Notes:

Restaurant:

My Experience:

Shopping:

Best Find:

The shop I want to go back to:

Museum:

The coolest thing I learned about this area:

Other:

Historic Areas

City: _____   **County:** _____

Plan your trip:

History:

Get the Facts

- ❑ Address_____
  _____
- ❑ Phone
- ❑ Best season to visit
  _____
- ❑ Pet Friendly   Y   N
- ❑ Reservations?   Y   N
  date made_____
- ❑ Distance from home
  miles: _____
  hours: _____

Things To Do:

- ❑ ADA availability
- ❑ Public Restrooms
- ❑ Gift Shop
- ❑ Museum
- ❑ Visitor Center
- ❑ Picnic areas
- ❑ Chamber of Commerce
- ❑ Monuments
- ❑ Art Galleries
- ❑ Tours
- ❑ Street Art
- ❑ Natural Areas
- ❑ Living History
- ❑ Cemetery
- ❑ Amphitheater

Places I Want to Visit in the Area:

Restaurants:
Boutiques & Shops:
Monuments:
Museums:

Budget for this trip:

Parking	$
Food	$
Museums	$
Hotel	$
Shopping	$
Total	$

Notes:

Restaurant:

My Experience:

Shopping:

Best Find:

The shop I want to go back to:

Museum:

The coolest thing I learned about this area:

Other:

Historic Areas

City: County:

Plan your trip:

History:

Things To Do:

- ❑ ADA availability
- ❑ Public Restrooms
- ❑ Gift Shop
- ❑ Museum
- ❑ Visitor Center
- ❑ Picnic areas
- ❑ Chamber of Commerce

- ❑ Monuments
- ❑ Art Galleries
- ❑ Tours
- ❑ Street Art
- ❑ Natural Areas
- ❑ Living History
- ❑ Cemetery
- ❑ Amphitheater

Places I Want to Visit in the Area:

Restaurants:

Boutiques & Shops:

Monuments:

Museums:

Get the Facts

- ❑ Address_____
- _____
- ❑ Phone
- ❑ Best season to visit
- _____
- ❑ Pet Friendly   Y   N
- ❑ Reservations?   Y   N
- date made_____
- ❑ Distance from home
- miles: _____
- hours: _____

Budget for this trip:

Parking	$
Food	$
Museums	$
Hotel	$
Shopping	$
Total	$

Notes:

Restaurant:

My Experience:

Shopping:

Best Find:

The shop I want to go back to:

Museum:

The coolest thing I learned about this area:

Other:

Historic Areas

City: County:

Plan your trip:

History:

Things To Do:

- ❑ ADA availability
- ❑ Public Restrooms
- ❑ Gift Shop
- ❑ Museum
- ❑ Visitor Center
- ❑ Picnic areas
- ❑ Chamber of Commerce
- ❑ Monuments
- ❑ Art Galleries
- ❑ Tours
- ❑ Street Art
- ❑ Natural Areas
- ❑ Living History
- ❑ Cemetery
- ❑ Amphitheater

Places I Want to Visit in the Area:

Restaurants:

Boutiques & Shops:

Monuments:

Museums:

Get the Facts

- ❑ Address_____
  _____
- ❑ Phone
- ❑ Best season to visit
  _____
- ❑ Pet Friendly   Y   N
- ❑ Reservations?   Y   N
  date made_____
- ❑ Distance from home
  miles: _____
  hours: _____

Budget for this trip:

Parking	$
Food	$
Museums	$
Hotel	$
Shopping	$
Total	$

Notes:

Restaurant:

My Experience:

Shopping:

Best Find:

The shop I want to go back to:

Museum:

The coolest thing I learned about this area:

Other:

Historic Areas

City: County:

Plan your trip:

History:

Things To Do:

- [ ] ADA availability
- [ ] Public Restrooms
- [ ] Gift Shop
- [ ] Museum
- [ ] Visitor Center
- [ ] Picnic areas
- [ ] Chamber of Commerce
- [ ] Monuments
- [ ] Art Galleries
- [ ] Tours
- [ ] Street Art
- [ ] Natural Areas
- [ ] Living History
- [ ] Cemetery
- [ ] Amphitheater

Places I Want to Visit in the Area:

Restaurants:

Boutiques & Shops:

Monuments:

Museums:

Get the Facts

- [ ] Address_____
  _____
- [ ] Phone
- [ ] Best season to visit
  _____
- [ ] Pet Friendly   Y   N
- [ ] Reservations?   Y   N
  date made_____
- [ ] Distance from home
  miles: _____
  hours: _____

Budget for this trip:

Parking	$
Food	$
Museums	$
Hotel	$
Shopping	$
Total	$

Notes:

Restaurant:

My Experience:

Shopping:

Best Find:

The shop I want to go back to:

Museum:

The coolest thing I learned about this area:

Other:

INDEX

SHA: *State Historic Area* SHP: *State Historic Park* SP: *State Park*

INDEX